FUNDAMENTALS
OF
BOTANY
SERIES

THE

PLANT

CELL

FUNDAMENTALS
OF
BOTANY
SERIES

edited by
WILLIAM A. JENSEN,
University of California
LEROY G. KAVALJIAN,
Sacramento State College

THE PLANT CELL
William A. Jensen, University of California

REPRODUCTION, HEREDITY, AND SEXUALITY
Stanton A. Cook, University of Oregon

NONVASCULAR PLANTS: FORM AND FUNCTION
William T. Doyle, Northwestern University

VASCULAR PLANTS: FORM AND FUNCTION
Frank B. Salisbury and Robert V. Parke, Colorado State University

PLANTS AND THE ECOSYSTEM
W. D. Billings, Duke University

EVOLUTION AND PLANTS OF THE PAST
Harlan C. Banks, Cornell University

PLANTS AND CIVILIZATION
Herbert G. Baker, University of California

William A. Jensen

UNIVERSITY OF CALIFORNIA

THE

PLANT

CELL

London
MACMILLAN AND CO., LTD.

FOREWORD

Because of the immensity and complexity of the field of botany, the great diversity of plants, and the many methods of plant study, the problem of how to present to the student the highlights of botanical knowledge gained over centuries is not easy to solve. The authors and editors of the volumes in this series believe that an understanding of plants—their parts, their activities, and their relationship to man—is of fundamental importance in appreciating the significance of life. To stress this concept, the form and function of plants, tissues, and cells are treated together. At all levels of organization, in each volume, information gathered by morphologists, physiologists, cytologists, taxonomists, geneticists, biochemists, and ecologists is combined.

Thus, in the volume on *The Plant Cell* by William A. Jensen, the structure and function of the various cell parts are discussed together —for example, mitochondria and respiration, photosynthesis and chloroplasts. The volume by Stanton A. Cook, *Reproduction, Heredity, and Sexuality,* combines the principles of genetics with the means of reproduction in the various plant groups. *Nonvascular Plants: Form and Function,* by William T. Doyle, and *Vascular Plants: Form and Function,* by Frank B. Salisbury and Robert V. Parke, cover the major plant groups and discuss the plants in terms of morphology, physiology, and biochemistry. The relation of plants, particularly vascular plants, to their environment and to each other is covered in *Plants and the Ecosystem* by W. D. Billings. The form and distribution of plants of the past and their relation to the concepts of evolution are considered by Harlan Banks in *Evolution and Plants of the Past.* Herbert G. Baker, in *Plants and Civilization,* discusses the importance of plants to man's social and economic development and the equally important consideration of man's role in the modification and distribution of plants.

In a series such as this, the editors are faced with the task of dividing a broad field into areas that can be presented in a meaningful way by the authors. There must be logic in the entire scheme, with few gaps and a minimum of overlap. Yet an instructor may not want to use the series of volumes in the sequence and manner preferred by the editors. Consequently, each volume must be usable alone and also in any sequence with the others. To achieve such a high degree of versatility is difficult, but we believe the series exhibits these features.

A concerted effort has been made by the authors and editors to maintain a consistent level of presentation. However, each author has been encouraged to approach his subject in his own way and to write in his own style in order to provide variety and to exploit the uniqueness of the individual author's viewpoint. Finally, while presenting the principles of botany we have tried to communicate the excitement of recent developments as well as the joy that comes with the extension of knowledge in any field.

The topic of this volume is the plant cell. Research has been extremely active in the area of cell structure and function, and within the past fifteen years our understanding of the cell has undergone a revolution due to new knowledge. The result of this surge of new information is a more complete understanding of the relation of structure to function at all levels of cell organization. This development is reflected in the organization of this volume. After the cell is introduced through a discussion of the historical development of our knowledge about it, each part of the cell is examined both for its form and for the biochemical processes associated with it. Mitosis, meiosis, and the genetic code are also considered. Finally, the problem of cell differentiation and development is discussed. In this treatment of the cell, every effort has been made to keep the discussions of biochemical and molecular phenomena within the grasp of the student without reducing the complexity of the systems to a point where explanations are essentially meaningless and understanding requires an act of faith. Of all the areas of biological research, none is moving so rapidly or in so exciting a fashion as that of the cell. This volume has been written to enable the student to use what he learns about the cell in his broader study of plants.

CONTENTS

Fifth printing: January 1967

MACMILLAN AND COMPANY LIMITED,
ST. MARTIN'S STREET, LONDON, W.C.2.
also
BOMBAY, CALCUTTA, MADRAS, MELBOURNE.
First published in the U.K. 1964.
©1964 by Wadsworth Publishing Company, Inc.,
Belmont, California. Printed in the United
States of America.

1

THE WORLD

OF THE CELL

Man's imagination has always been captivated by the thought of unexplored worlds, of lands and planets other than our own. The cell is a wonderful world discovered almost three hundred years ago and still but partially explored. This is the world—a complex, fascinating, and often beautiful world—that will be considered in this volume. The major aim will be to examine the cell and its parts as a combination of form and function. We will first consider the development of knowledge about the cell.

The first drawings of cells seen by the early microscopists were like the first tentative maps of the coastline of the New World. As the explorers became more daring and their methods better, the maps became more detailed and accurate. Eventually, all the more obvious features of the land were recognized and recorded. Still newer methods were then required to obtain a more complete, more meaningful knowledge of the region. The history of cytology, the science of the cell, follows a similar pattern.

Robert Hooke, using one of the earliest microscopes, first described the cell in 1665. He saw only one part of the cell, the cell wall (Fig. 1-1a). He drew a likeness of cells that he saw in a piece of cork under the microscope. Hooke realized that the cells of cork were dead and that living cells, which he saw in leaves, contained "juices." A few years later, Anton van Leeuwenhoek, the famous Dutch microscopist, saw green-colored bodies in the cells of plants (Fig. 1-1b). These bodies are now known as *chloroplasts*. Thus, by 1700 the plant cell was known to be composed of a wall and to contain "juices" and chloroplasts.

The next major advance came in 1833 when Robert Brown, in England, discovered that all cells contain a rather large body that he

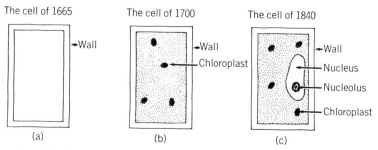

Fig. 1-1. *Development of knowledge about the cell from 1665 to 1840.*

termed the *nucleus* (Fig. 1-1c). Shortly after, in Germany, Matthias Schleiden found a smaller body within the nucleus and called it the *nucleolus.*

These discoveries followed the development of better microscopes and microscopic techniques. The relation of microscope development to advances in knowledge is dramatically illustrated several times in the history of cytology. One such period occurred in the last half of the 1800s with the development of the present-day light microscope and associated microtechnique. The microscope Robert Brown used to observe nuclei, while better designed mechanically, was not significantly improved optically over those used by Hooke and Leeuwenhoek. Only after a means of producing better lenses was discovered, mainly through the work of Ernst Abbe, could magnifications over a thousand times be obtained. Developments in the handling of tissue accompanied these improvements in the microscope.

The effective use of the microscope hinges on light passing through the material to be examined. Most tissues are opaque and must be cut into thin sections before enough light can pass through for observations to be made. Some tissues can be sectioned with a razor but most must be infiltrated and surrounded with a matrix that acts to hold the material for sectioning. A special machine, a microtome, is used to cut the tissue into uniform sections. But once the sections are obtained, a new difficulty arises: the natural contrast of the various parts of the tissue is not great enough for much to be seen. To remedy this difficulty, the sections must be stained with dyes that react with the different parts of the cell, vastly increasing their contrast. The development of all of these procedures in the last half of the nineteenth century led to an astonishingly detailed knowledge of the cell based on the light microscope.

The concept that all organisms are composed of cells appeared early in this period of intensive exploration of the cell. A clear statement of this idea by Matthias Schleiden and Theodor Schwann in 1838 summarized the thinking of the period and, with some exceptions, is still valid today. If all organisms consist of cells, the question that next arises is "Where do these cells come from?" This question was heatedly argued and actively investigated during the middle of the nineteenth century and was answered by Rudolf Virchow in 1858: "Cells come only from cells." Thus, new cells arise only by the division of an existing cell.

The mechanism of this division was established by the 1870s (Fig. 1-2a, b). Through the work of many brilliant cytologists it be-

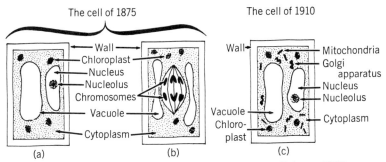

Fig. 1-2. *Development of knowledge about the cell from 1875 to 1910.*

came known that when a cell is about to divide, changes occur in the nucleus. Dense bodies known as chromosomes appear, and the membrane limiting the nucleus disappears. Each type of organism was found to have a fixed number of chromosomes that divide during the process of nuclear division or *mitosis*. During mitosis the chromosomes duplicate and separate, each group reconstituting a new nucleus. Each new nucleus now contains the same number of chromosomes as the original nucleus. The cell then divides by the formation of a new cell wall between the two new nuclei.

During and shortly after this period, a second type of cell division was discovered. In this type of division the chromosome number is not faithfully reproduced but is reduced to precisely one-half. Frequently such divisions were found associated with reproductive cells and resulted in cells having one-half the usual number of chromosomes found in that organism. The fusion of two such cells would restore the original chromosome number. This type of division is called *meiosis* and is of great importance in heredity and reproduction. From 1880 to 1920 the investigations of a large number of brilliant cytologists and geneticists using all types of organisms elucidated many aspects of chromosome structure and behavior as well as the nature and actions of the genes. The role of the genes in the control of development was defined and investigated. Other parts of the cell, although investigated to be sure, could not compete with the fascination of the genes and chromosomes for an equal share of the cytologists' attention.

As microscopic observations continued, more parts of the cell were seen (Fig. 1-2c). These parts include the *mitochondria*—small spheres, rods, or filaments—and the *Golgi apparatus*. Knowledge of the cell continued to increase and it became clear that the cell is divided into a watery region or *vacuole,* which occupies the central region, and a dense peripheral layer of *cytoplasm*. The nucleus, chloroplasts, mitochondria, and the other particulate parts of the cell are in the cytoplasm, which is separated from the wall on one side and the vacuole on the other by membranes.

By 1900 the cell had been explored to the point where its major landmarks were known. The functions of the cell parts were a different matter. Little was known of them except that chloroplasts had been shown to be the site of photosynthesis. A major advance occurred in the knowledge of the cell in the early 1900s when it became clear that the genes, which are the units of inheritance, are associated with the chromosomes. This discovery shifted emphasis in cytological research to the study of the nucleus and the chromosomes—an emphasis that remained one of the dominant features of cytology for thirty years.

While the functions of the various cell parts remained generally unknown, knowledge of the chemistry of the cell increased. Organic chemistry developed during the 1800s and various investigators attempted, with considerable success, to apply this new knowledge to the cell. The development of the concept of the cell was paralleled by the development of the concept of the molecule. While much exploratory work on cell chemistry was done during the 1800s and the broad outlines of cell composition became understood, a genuine synthesis of biochemistry and cytology did not occur until the 1940s and '50s.

The biochemists, who were applying and extending the discoveries of organic chemistry to the cell, were essentially treating the cell as a homogeneous mass of chemical compounds. Their principal aim was to remove these chemicals from the cell and to study them in as pure a condition as possible. The cytologists, on the other hand, continued to study the cell by examining it under the microscope, using techniques that made it virtually impossible to study the function of its parts. In the late 1930s a series of advances in techniques made it possible to synthesize these two fields, leading to an increased knowledge of the cell as a functional unit and not merely as a physical entity.

One of the procedures developed during this period was that of cell homogenization and the separation of the various cell parts by various means. Selected parts of the cell could then be isolated and analyzed individually. Moreover, some parts retained part of their biochemical activities, which then could be studied by biochemical methods. Not all parts of the cell could be approached in this manner, but for some of the most important parts, a great deal could be learned.

Another set of procedures that were developed during this period were the cytochemical methods. These allow the identification of chemical components and activities of the cell directly on the cellular level. Cytochemical methods were first devised in the early 1800s but were vastly improved and extended in the late 1930s and the '40s.

From these improved methods came a more complete knowledge of cell composition and the function of cell parts. One of the first and most important of the findings using these methods was that the mitochondria are the sites of aerobic respiration. In the process of aerobic respiration, the cell, through the utilization of sugar in the presence of oxygen, obtains most of the energy it requires for life. In the chloroplast, light energy is converted to chemical energy and incorporated into sugar molecules through the process of photosynthesis. In mitochondria, the chemical energy in the sugar molecule is converted to other forms of energy more readily available to the cell through the process of respiration.

Many additional discoveries were made using these procedures, including the finding that protein synthesis occurs primarily in the cytoplasm. This is extremely important, because protein molecules form a large portion of the cell and, in addition, all enzymes are proteins. Enzymes are the all-important organic catalysts that regulate most reactions occurring in the cell.

Protein synthesis was found to be linked to submicroscopic particles now termed *ribosomes*. These particles consist of protein and ribonucleic acid (RNA). Two kinds of nucleic acids had been known to exist in the cell for many years: deoxyribonucleic acid (DNA), which is found primarily in the nucleus of the cell as part of the chromosomes; and RNA, which is found in the nucleus, as part of the nucleolus, and in the cytoplasm of the cell.

One of the great triumphs of modern cytology and biochemistry has been the elucidation of the relationship of the nucleic acids to protein synthesis. This has included the realization that DNA is the genetic material and that RNA is the means by which the genetic information is transmitted to the cytoplasm where it influences the production of proteins. Thus, the activity of the cell can be understood through analysis of the molecules involved, and the ultimate synthesis of cytology and chemistry is close to being achieved.

During the past two decades, exciting developments have been taking place in other areas of cytology, particularly in those areas concerned with cell structure. Knowledge of cell structure is largely (but not solely) dependent on what can be seen with the use of various aids to human vision. The light microscope was the first such aid and reached the peak of its perfection around 1900. The ultimate limit of resolution of the microscope is determined by the properties of light and not by the skill of the men making the instrument. Knowledge of the cell was therefore limited to objects over 0.3 micron (μ; 1000

The cell of 1960

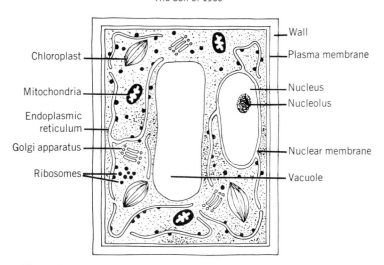

Fig. 1-3. *Diagrammatic summary of the major components of the cell as understood in 1960. The various cell parts are not drawn in correct proportion to one another.*

microns = 1 millimeter). Moreover, the internal structure of the smaller cell parts could not be observed.

The development of the electron microscope surmounted this difficulty, because a beam of electrons instead of a beam of light is used. Where the upper magnification of the light microscope is 1200 times, the upper magnification of the electron microscope is 160,000 times. To use the electron microscope, microscopists had to devise new techniques that permitted the observation of extremely thin sections of a cell. With the use of these techniques and the electron microscope,

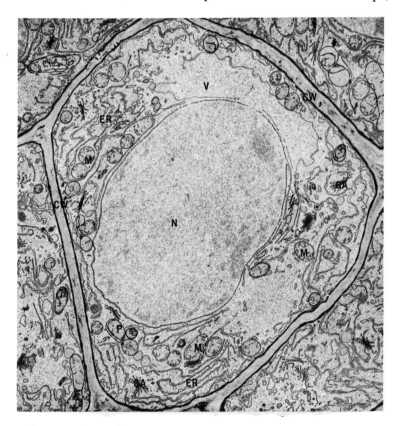

Fig. 1-4. *Plant cell as seen with the electron microscope. CW: cell wall; ER: endoplasmic reticulum; GA: Golgi apparatus; M: mitochondria; N: nucleus; P: plastid. This preparation does not show the ribosomes, chromatin, or nucleolus. Compare with Fig. 7-1.*

we can see structures that are measured not in microns but in angstroms (1 micron = 10,000 angstroms [A]).

These techniques have added a new dimension to the knowledge of the organization of the cell (Fig. 1-3). Mitochondria, chloroplasts, and Golgi bodies have been found to contain elaborate internal structures. New cell parts have been discovered. The most spectacular of these is the *endoplasmic reticulum,* a folded, sheet-like structure that permeates the cytoplasm of the cell (Fig. 1-4). Also seen for the first time were individual ribosomes, which had previously been known only from centrifugation studies.

Continued exploration of the cell with ever more sophisticated tools and methods has resulted in a constant growth of knowledge about the cell. The keynote of modern cytology is an understanding of both the structure and function of the various cell parts and how these parts are integrated into the whole functional cell. This volume undertakes to present an introduction to modern cytology and is an invitation to explore the fascinating world of the cell.

2

WALL,

MEMBRANE,

AND VACUOLE

THE CELL WALL

Plant cells, with few exceptions, possess walls. These walls are an outstanding characteristic of the plant cell and determine many features of the plant, including the mode of cell division and growth.

Cell walls vary greatly in composition and morphology. Both of these characteristics frequently have a close relationship to the age and function of the cell. A young cell, undergoing division and elongation, is surrounded by a single wall called the *primary* wall. The primary wall is frequently thin (1 to 3 μ thick) and elastic, increasing greatly in area as the cell grows. As growth ceases, a *secondary* wall, different in composition and physical properties, is laid down between the cytoplasm and the primary wall. The secondary wall is most often thick (5-10 μ) and rigid, giving great tensile strength to the cell. All cells have a primary wall but not all have a secondary wall. Examples of cells with unusually prominent secondary walls are found in the vascular and supportive tissues of the plant.

The spatial relation of the primary and secondary walls as seen in the light microscope is shown in Figs. 2-1 and 2-2. The primary walls of two cells are joined by a common layer, the *middle lamella*. This layer functions as an intracellular matrix which holds groups of cells together. Also shown in Fig. 2-1 are *pits,* which are essentially holes in the wall and may be either simple in appearance, as shown in Fig. 2-2, or highly complex, in which case they are termed *bordered* pits.

When the wall is carefully examined with the light microscope, it can occasionally be resolved into a series of layers. These layers are

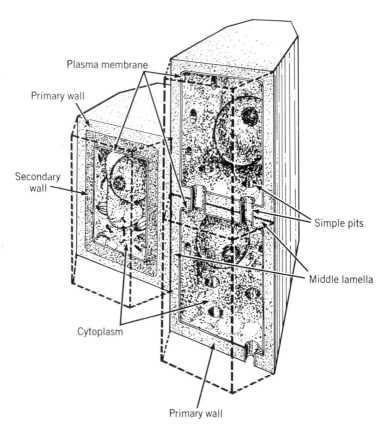

Plasma membrane

Primary wall

Secondary wall

Simple pits

Middle lamella

Cytoplasm

Primary wall

Fig. 2-1. *Diagram of the various cell walls and their relation to the remaining parts of the cell.*

difficult to see, and few details of the fine structure of the wall can be observed. With the electron microscope, however, much of the ultra-structure of the wall can be seen and studied in detail (Fig. 2-3). The wall is composed of strands of material called *microfibrils*. Between these microfibrils there is a matrix, which does not appear in Fig. 2-3 because it was removed during the course of preparing the wall for observation in the electron microscope. The relation of the matrix to the microfibrils can be seen in Fig. 2-4.

The diagram in Fig. 2-4 indicates further that the microfibrils can be resolved by physical and chemical means into long chains of

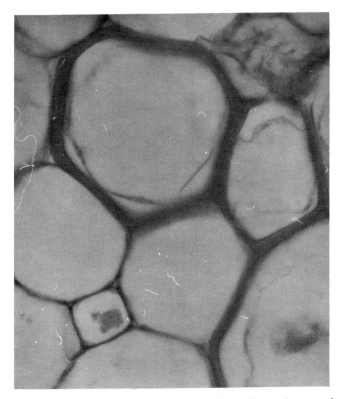

Fig. 2-2. *Photomicrograph of the cell walls in* Hoja *showing the appearance of the primary and secondary walls when viewed in cross section.*

cellulose molecules. These in turn are composed of repeating units of *glucose molecules.* Glucose is a sugar containing six carbon atoms, twelve hydrogen atoms, and six oxygen atoms. The way this assortment of carbon, hydrogen, and oxygen atoms is joined together to form glucose is shown in Fig. 2-4. For simplicity in depicting the glucose molecule as a unit in a cellulose molecule, it is common to show only the carbon atoms, or, even more simply, to draw an outline of the structure omitting all the atoms.

The cellulose molecule is an important one in the structure of the plant cell. Composed of thousands of repeating glucose units, it is the major structural element of the wall and, particularly in the case of the primary wall, gives most of the actual strength to the wall. Cellulose is the first example encountered here of a giant molecule, composed of

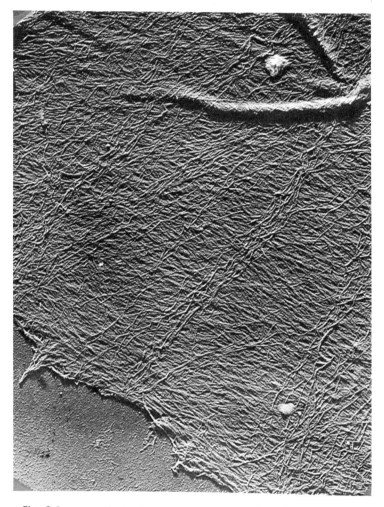

Fig. 2-3. *Microfibrils of the primary cell wall, visible in an electron-microscope photograph. Courtesy of Dr. M. Forman.*

repeating units, so frequently found in cells. Such molecules include the proteins and nucleic acids that are composed of more complex and varied repeating units than those found in cellulose. Moreover, in these compounds the units are joined together in different patterns. They are similar to cellulose, however, in being giant molecules. The significance to the cell of these large molecules composed of smaller repeating units is great. As a group they not only form the structural

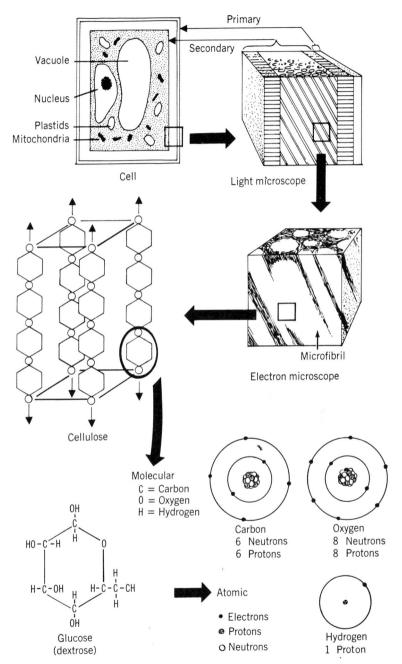

Fig. 2-4. *Cell wall from the microscopic to the submicroscopic to the molecular level.*

elements of the cell, but they also permit the retention and transfer of information necessary to the functioning of the cell.

Cellulose is a carbohydrate and, because glucose is a sugar (or *saccharide*) and cellulose is composed of many glucose molecules, cellulose is also a *polysaccharide*. There are many other sugars and polysaccharides found in the cell and in the cell wall. The wall also contains polysaccharides composed of repeating units of sugars with five carbon atoms rather than six, as in glucose. Because glucose has six carbon atoms it is called a *hexose;* sugars with five carbon atoms are called *pentoses*. There are hexoses other than glucose because there are several different ways in which the same number of hydrogen, oxygen, and carbon atoms can be arranged to give molecules having different characteristics.

Pentose polysaccharides are found in the hemicellulose compounds of the wall. Relatively little is known concerning hemicellulose except that it is part of the matrix between the cellulose microfibrils and forms a significant proportion of the walls of many cell types.

Other chemical components of the primary wall and the middle lamella are the *pectic* substances. These are large molecules made up of repeating units called *hexuronic acids* (Fig. 2-5). Hexuronic acids are derivatives of hexose sugars. The pectic substances vary in physical properties but all are long chains of hexuronic acids. The middle lamella appears to be composed primarily of pectic substances. The removal of the pectic substances from a tissue causes the cells to fall apart. The separate cells retain their shape because other wall materials are still present and strong enough to retain their original form.

The middle lamella and the primary wall in a young cell are composed primarily of cellulose, hemicellulose, and the pectic substances. All of these compounds are either carbohydrates or carbohydrate de-

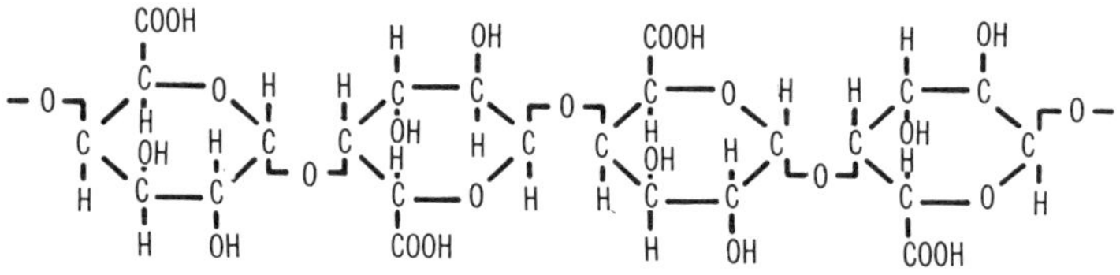

Fig. 2-5. *Chemical structure of pectin.*

rivatives. When the cell matures and the secondary wall develops, a new wall component, called *lignin,* appears. Lignin is not related to the carbohydrate compounds. The chemical structure of lignin is not completely understood but it is known to be composed also of repeating units. These units are complex and joined in a manner that provides great tensile strength (Fig. 2-6). When lignin is present in a wall, the wall is usually strong and rigid. The strength and rigidity of wood, for example, is a result of lignified cell walls.

Lignin does not appear to occur in the form of microfibrils, as does cellulose, but forms a part of the matrix surrounding the cellulose microfibrils. Moreover, lignin is not found alone in the wall but is always found associated with cellulose. While secondary walls are particularly heavy in lignin content, especially in woody plants, lignin also occurs in the primary wall and the middle lamella of mature cells.

Still other compounds are found in the walls of many cells or in certain organisms. Chief among these are the waxes found in the walls

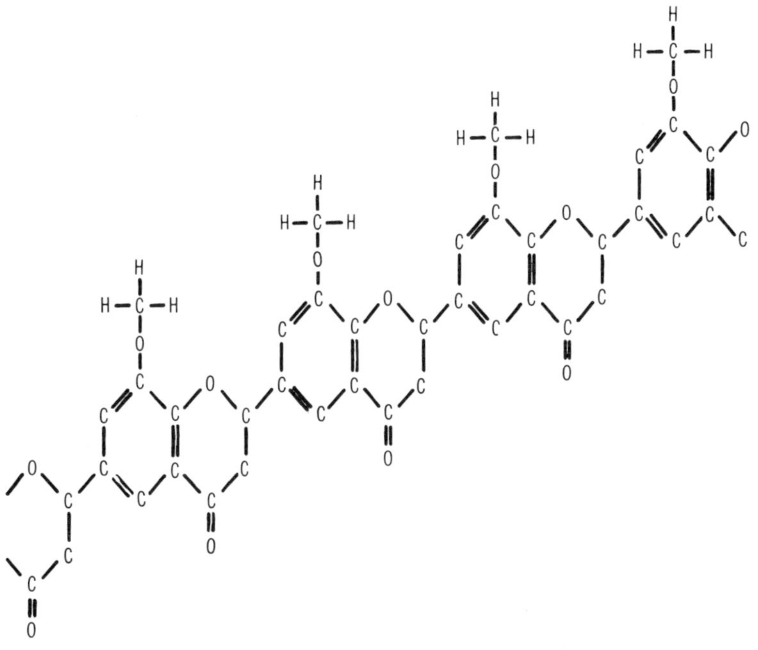

Fig. 2-6. *Possible chemical structure of lignin. Only the major ring structure is shown.*

of cells constituting the surface layers of the plant. Waxes are found in many cells and are important in the function of these cells. The walls of many fungi contain *chitin,* a carbohydrate wall component which is also found in the exoskeleton of insects. Another substance present in the walls of the cells of many grasses and horsetails is *silica,* which is the principal component of sand and glass. In the cell walls of bacteria and blue-green algae, complex combinations of material occur; they include large amounts of amino acids and proteins.

The wall is a complex structure composed of many chemical substances arranged in a highly organized manner. How is it formed? Relatively little is known of the synthesizing mechanisms involved in the formation of the various chemical components of the wall. Less is known concerning the way these units are actually built into a wall. But through careful studies employing the electron microscope and special physical methods using the light microscope, some information is available on the way walls are formed.

When the walls of young cells are examined under the electron microscope, the microfibrils are seen to extend in all directions with little or no orientation (Fig. 2-3). As the cell grows, more layers of microfibrils are deposited but in a more organized manner, and they show a definite orientation. Layer upon layer is added as the cell grows until the wall reaches its final thickness. The earliest layers are stretched during the enlargement phase of cell growth, yet, because more layers are added, wall thickness remains the same or increases. This process is known as growth by *apposition.*

There are some cells in which wall development does not appear to occur solely by apposition. In these cells, new microfibrils are believed to be inserted throughout the wall, not merely at the surface. Such growth is called *intercalary* growth. Finally, some cells grow only at the ends, not throughout their length. This type of growth is found in developing root hairs and growing pollen tubes and is known as *tip* growth.

How the microfibrils are formed, the relation of the cell membrane to wall formation, and the site of synthesis of the units are all unsolved problems. The formation of the wall is of great importance, and an understanding of cell growth depends to a great extent on an appreciation of the method of synthesis of this remarkable structure.

THE PLASMA MEMBRANE

Surrounding the cytoplasm of the cell, and delimiting the cytoplasm from the wall, is the *plasma membrane* (Fig. 2-7). This structure,

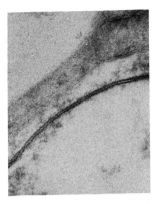

Fig. 2-7. *Plasma membrane as seen in the electron microscope. Courtesy of Dr. J. McAlear, U. of California, Berkeley.*

common to both plant and animal cells, is completely different from the wall in form, composition, and function. Thus, whereas the wall is a rigid, relatively thick structure, the plasma membrane is a thin (approximately 75 angstroms [A]), flexible structure not directly visible in the light microscope. The membrane is composed of protein and lipid, whereas the wall is predominantly carbohydrate in nature. The wall provides support, whereas the plasma membrane is the outer limit of the cytoplasm of the cell and regulates the movement of substances into and out of the cell.

The *proteins* that compose the plasma membrane are large molecules assembled from amino acid molecules. In this way they resemble the polysaccharides, but they differ from them in three ways: (1) in the nature of the basic unit (amino acids instead of sugars); (2) in the variety of the kinds of basic units per molecule (in cellulose only one sugar, glucose, is present, while in most proteins any number of the twenty different naturally occurring amino acids may be present); and (3) in the way the basic units are joined (proteins are far more complicated molecules than polysaccharides). Proteins are one of the most important classes of chemical components found in the cell, and will be discussed in several other chapters.

Lipids are also important molecules with regard to cell function. As in the case of the polysaccharides and proteins, lipids are molecules composed of unit molecules—in this case, fatty acid molecules. Lipids, unlike proteins, are water-insoluble, but they can be dissolved in organic solvents such as alcohol, acetone, and ether.

There is considerable evidence to indicate that the molecules of protein and lipid are arranged in the membrane as shown in Fig. 2-8.

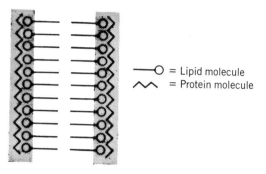

—○ = Lipid molecule

∧∧ = Protein molecule

Fig. 2-8. *Possible arrangement of protein and lipid molecules in the cell membrane.*

The protein molecules are aligned on the exterior of the membrane and are bound to the lipid molecules, which occupy the center. At extremely high magnifications with the electron microscope, such an arrangement is seen as two dark lines, each 25 A wide, with a light central area, also 25 A wide, and is called a *unit* membrane. The unit membrane, composed of protein and lipid, is of great importance in the architecture of the cell and will be encountered repeatedly in discussions of the various cell parts. The interrelation of the plasma membrane, the endoplasmic reticulum, and the nuclear membrane is apparent in Fig. 2-9, and will be discussed at greater length in later chapters. Under the electron microscope, the various membranes in the cell are similar in appearance, but this similarity does not imply that they all have the same properties or the same function.

The plasma membrane is the layer that maintains the integrity of the cell in relation to the surrounding environment. It is able to do this because it acts as a differentially permeable barrier—a barrier that prevents the organic materials of the cell, such as sugars and soluble protein, from leaking out of the cell while permitting water and salts to enter. This differentially permeable nature of the membrane is the key to its chief function. If the membrane were completely permeable, too much of the cell contents could simply dissolve out of the cell, and the vital functions of the cell would cease. If the membrane were completely impermeable, water, salts, and other materials essential for the metabolism of the cell could not enter, and again the vital functions of the cell would cease. Thus, the cell must be surrounded by a differentially permeable membrane in order to live.

The differentially permeable character of the membrane has other consequences for the cell. One of these is the phenomenon of *osmosis*.

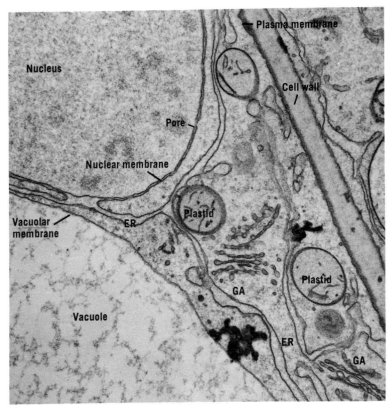

Fig. 2-9. *Relation of the cell membrane, the endoplasmic reticulum, and the nuclear envelope in a plant cell.*

All molecules, because of their kinetic energy, are in constant movement and will diffuse from regions of higher concentration to regions of lower concentration of the molecule being considered. Actually, it is more correct to say that molecules diffuse in response to a gradient in the free energy of the molecules. The free energy of the molecules, say of water, is influenced by many factors. One of these factors is the interaction with other molecules. Thus, in the case of water, the water molecules inside the cell will have a lower free-energy level because of the presence of materials dissolved in the water. Under these conditions, water will diffuse into the cell. As diffusion continues, the free-energy level of the water in the cell increases and there is a buildup of pressure. When the free energy of the water molecules inside the cell equals that of the water molecules outside the cell, there is no further net gain of water by the cell. Thus, osmosis results in the movement of water into the cell and the buildup of pressure, which forces the cytoplasm against the wall.

If the cell is placed in a solution in which there are large numbers of dissolved molecules, the free-energy level will be lower outside the cell than inside. Under these conditions, water will diffuse from the cell and the cytoplasm will contract and pull away from the wall. When this occurs, the cell is described as being *plasmolyzed*.

The movement of water in and out of the cell is, consequently, a physical phenomenon that does not involve the active metabolism of the cell. Some salts move into the cell in essentially the same manner. There are examples, however, where the cell expends metabolic energy to transport materials across the cell membrane. The mechanism of such transport is not clearly understood. There is evidence,

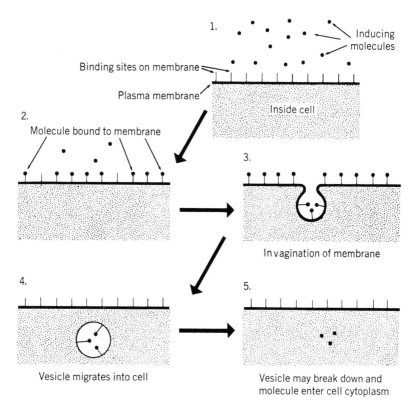

Fig. 2-10. *Diagrammatic representation of pinocytosis.*

however, that such transport may involve a carrier system. A carrier is specific for the substance to be transported and is postulated to pick up the substance on the external surface of the plasma membrane and carry it to the internal surface. The carrier can also transport material in the opposite direction. Involved either directly or indirectly is the expenditure of energy. A wide range of substances, including both inorganic ions and carbohydrates, are believed to enter and leave the cell through a carrier mechanism. Clearly, some such mechanism must be involved where the concentration of a substance is greater in the cell than in the surrounding medium. A classic example of accumulation against a concentration gradient is found in certain marine algae, which may maintain an internal concentration of iodine a million times greater than the concentration in the sea water that surrounds them.

Another mechanism that is responsible for the active uptake of substances is *pinocytosis*. In pinocytosis the cell membrane invaginates and forms small vesicles within the cytoplasm of the cell (Fig. 2-10). The material contained in the vesicle is finally utilized by the cell. Pinocytosis is known to occur in various animal and fungal cells, and is believed to be possible in some cells in vascular plants. The process of pinocytosis demonstrates that the cell membrane is not a simple physical barrier but is the outer membrane of a living cell.

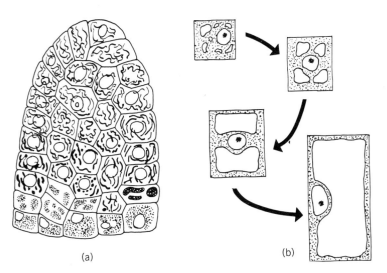

(a)

(b)

Fig. 2-11. *Development of the vacuole on a microscopic level.* (*a*) *Cells of rose leaves.* (*b*) *Barley root cells.*

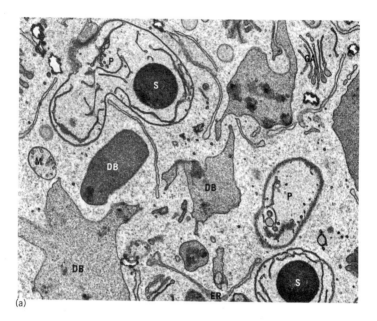

(a)

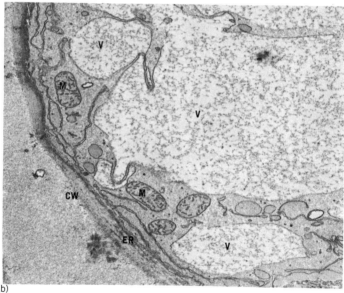

(b)

Fig. 2-12. (*a*) *Electron-microscope photograph of the dense bodies that occur in the cytoplasm of plant cells and that may represent the early stages of vacuole development.* (*b*) *A later stage in the development of the vacuole. Courtesy of Dr. H. Mollenhauer, U. of Texas.*

THE CELL VACUOLE

The *vacuole* is almost as distinctive a feature of many plant cells as is the wall. In a mature plant cell, the vacuole may occupy 90 per cent of the volume of the cell. The cytoplasm and nucleus in such a cell are pressed against the cell wall by the large central vacuole.

The vacuole is surrounded by a membrane. This membrane prevents the mixing of the contents of the vacuole with the cytoplasm. Like the plasma membrane, the vacuolar membrane is a single-unit membrane and similar to it in appearance in the electron microscope. While the vacuolar membrane appears similar in form to the plasma membrane, it has different properties. For example, the two membranes have different permeability and physiological characteristics.

The major component of large vacuoles is water. Salts, sugars, and pigments, as well as other substances, may be dissolved in the water. The concentration of such materials may become very great, with the result that salt crystals may form or the vacuole may become highly colored. The red color of many flowers—roses, for example—is a result of pigments concentrated in the vacuoles of the petals of the flower. The vacuole may also be strongly acidic, as in citrus fruits. The acid content of the vacuole may be so great that if the vacuolar sap makes contact with the cytoplasm, the cytoplasm will be severely damaged.

In young cells, the vacuoles are inconspicuous and may not be visible with the light microscope. Vacuoles that are visible in young cells are small and numerous. As the cell becomes larger and older, the vacuoles enlarge and coalesce (Fig. 2-11). When the cell reaches maturity, there is frequently only one large vacuole present. The origin of vacuoles in young cells is not clear. Evidence from electron microscopy indicates that in young cells there are dense-appearing, irregularly shaped bodies (Fig. 2-12), which become less dense and more regular in shape as the cell develops. These bodies may be young vacuoles. A membrane surrounding these bodies can be seen at this point. The vacuoles continue to enlarge and merge until the mature vacuole is formed.

3

CHLOROPLASTS

AND

PHOTOSYNTHESIS

ENERGY AND LIFE

Life is a fragile, unstable thing, maintained only through the ceaseless operation of hundreds of reactions that continually build and maintain the living system. These reactions require energy. Energy— its utilization, transformation, and transportation—is a major activity of the cell. Many of the chemical constituents of the cell are devoted to energy conversion reactions; two cell organelles—the *plastids* and the *mitochondria*—are primarily concerned with energy conversion.

The ultimate source of energy available to organisms living on the earth is light, or electromagnetic energy. This energy is transformed into chemical energy through *photosynthesis*. The biological conversion of light energy into chemical energy occurs only in green plants and a few bacteria. Photosynthesis is the reaction on which life as it exists today is based. Without it, all cells, whether plant or animal, would ultimately be deprived of usable energy and would die.

The site of photosynthesis in the plant cell is the chloroplast. The existence of chloroplasts has been known since the 1700s, and they have been known as the site of photosynthesis since the mid-1800s. Actually, the chloroplasts are only one of a class of cell organelles called the *plastids*.

THE PLASTIDS

The plastids are as distinctive a feature of the plant cell as the wall and the vacuole. The chloroplasts are the best known of this group of cell organelles that show similarity to one another while also exhibiting marked differences. In addition to the chloroplasts, which contain

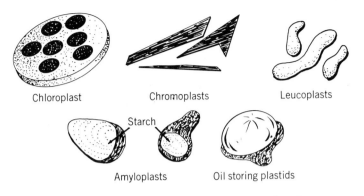

Fig. 3-1. *Examples of various types of plastids.*

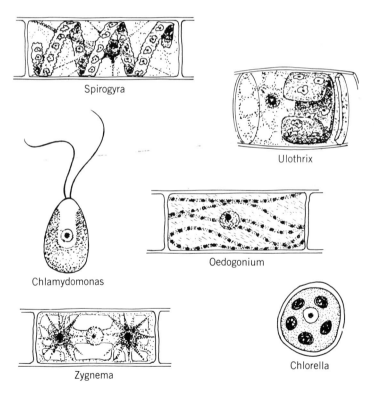

Fig. 3-2. *Types of chloroplasts found in the algae.*

the green pigment chlorophyll, the plastids include the brightly colored *chromoplasts*, which contain pigments other than chlorophyll, the colorless *leucoplasts*, and the various plastids that function primarily in food storage. Finally, there are the *proplastids*, which are generally assumed to be young or immature plastids.

When examined under the microscope, the plastids are seen to have a wide variety of forms (Fig. 3-1). Whereas the proplastids are usually small, the chromoplasts may be large or small and may take the form of plates, spirals, or discs. Although the chloroplasts of the mosses, ferns, and seed plants are quite similar, being disc-shaped, the chloroplasts of different species of algae may be in the form of spherical bands, perforated sheets, stars, cups, or discs (Fig. 3-2).

THE STRUCTURE OF THE CHLOROPLAST

The size of the disc-shaped chloroplast present in the mosses, ferns, and seed plants is roughly 2 to 4 microns in diameter and 0.5 to 1 micron in thickness. Examined with the highest magnifications of the light microscope, the chloroplasts frequently appear granular. The dense areas visible are called *grana,* while the lighter areas are termed *stroma.*

When chloroplasts—particularly sectioned chloroplasts—are examined with the electron microscope, a beautiful and elaborate internal structure can be observed (Fig. 3-3). The chloroplast is seen

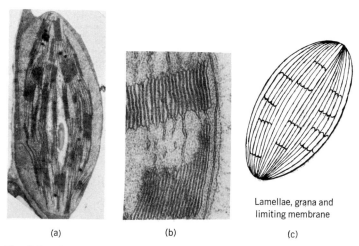

Lamellae, grana and limiting membrane

(a)   (b)   (c)

Fig. 3-3. *Electron-microscope photograph of the chloroplast of a vascular plant. (a) Bean. (b) Tobacco. Courtesy of Dr. Elliot Weir, U. of California, Davis.*

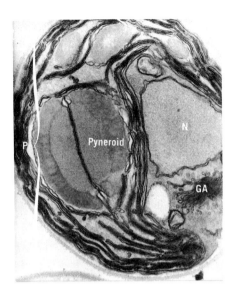

Lamellae and limiting
membrane

Fig. 3-4. *Electron-microscope photograph of a chloroplast from a green alga, Chlorella. Courtesy of Dr. Roderick Park, U. of California, Berkeley.*

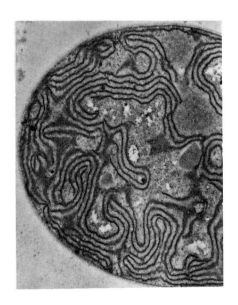

Photosynthetic membranes
in cytoplasm

Fig. 3-5. *Electron-microscope photograph of a blue-green alga, Anabaena. Courtesy of Dr. Norma Lang, U. of California, Davis.*

to be bounded by a double membrane that delimits it from the cytoplasm. Within the chloroplast there is an elaborate series of membranes that lie parallel to one another and extend throughout the length of the chloroplast. These membranes are termed *lamellae*. At intervals throughout the lamellae, additional layers of membrane-producing areas of greater density are interspersed. These areas are the grana seen with the light microscope.

All chloroplasts do not have the same internal structure. The plastids of the mosses, ferns, and seed plants are generally like that shown in Fig. 3-3. The green and brown algae have plastids consisting of a double limiting membrane and lamellae but lacking grana (Fig. 3-4). In the blue-green algae, no limiting membrane exists, and parallel membranes containing the photosynthetic pigments extend directly in the cytoplasm (Fig. 3-5).

THE COMPOSITION OF CHLOROPLASTS

Chloroplasts can be isolated by grinding leaves in a weak sugar solution with sand. The cell wall and membrane are ruptured, releasing the cell contents. By centrifuging this suspension of cell parts at different speeds, the various parts can be sedimented to the bottom of the centrifuge tube in a relatively pure state. Such isolated chloroplasts can be analyzed and their chemical composition determined.

When chloroplasts are chemically analyzed, they are found to consist predominantly of proteins, lipids, and pigments, with some ribonucleic acid (RNA). The RNA is in the form of small particles that occur between the lamellae. These are particularly clear in dark-grown chloroplasts. Deoxyribonucleic acid (DNA) may also be present in some chloroplasts, but the extent to which it is present, both in amount and occurrence, has not yet been determined. Much of the protein present is in the form of *enzyme* molecules. Enzymes are the organic catalysts that regulate most biological reactions; they will be discussed more fully later. The lipids are found almost entirely in the lamellar portions of the chloroplast and structure of the membranes.

The most distinctive chemical components of the chloroplasts are the pigments. Two major classes of pigments are present in all chloroplasts: *chlorophylls* and *carotenoids*.

The chemical structure of chlorophyll *a* is shown in Fig. 3-6. The molecule consists of a flat head, composed of four repeating units

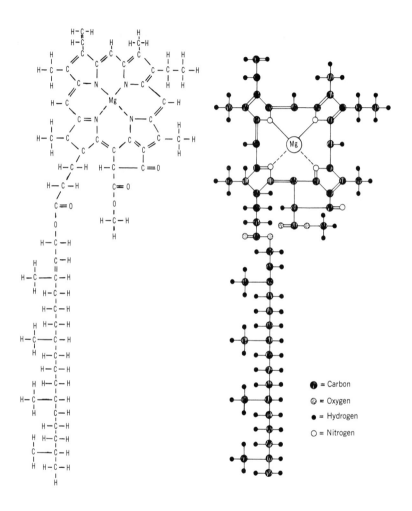

Fig. 3-6. *Chemical structure of chlorophyll* a.

surrounding a magnesium atom, and a long tail. The general form of the chlorophyll molecule is similar to the heme portion of hemoglobin, in which iron replaces the magnesium.

There are always two photosynthetic pigments present in a chloroplast. One is always chlorophyll *a*. The other may be one of the modified versions of chlorophyll *a*, such as chlorophyll *b*. The second pigment need not be a chlorophyll and may be one of the accessory pigments, such as *phycobilin,* found in some algae.

Carotenoids are yellow pigments that are widely found in chloroplasts. They may also occur alone in chromoplasts. The yellow color of carrots is due to the presence of carotenoid-containing chromoplasts. Carotenoids are the source of vitamin A for animals. The molecular structure of the carotenoids is quite different from that of the chlorophylls, being a long sausage-shaped arrangement of atoms (Fig. 3-7). Together these pigments are localized in the lamella and make up approximately 15 per cent of these structures.

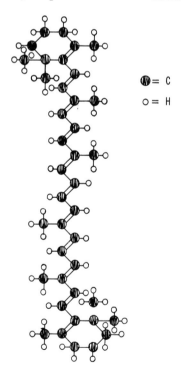

$\bullet = C$

$\circ = H$

Fig. 3-7. *Chemical structure of a carotenoid.*

Other pigments may be present in chloroplasts, particularly in the algae. The chlorophylls and carotenoids are universally present and of great importance in the process of photosynthesis.

PHOTOSYNTHESIS

The primary function of the chloroplast is in photosynthesis. The proof for such a claim is simple: cells without chloroplasts do not carry on photosynthesis. The only exceptions are the blue-green algae, which have the essential parts of chloroplasts but do not have them organized as discrete bodies, and the photosynthetic bacteria. A corollary of the statement that cells without chloroplasts do not carry on photosynthesis is that isolated chloroplasts can carry on photosynthesis.

Photosynthesis is the conversion of light energy into chemical energy. This conversion involves the synthesis of carbohydrate from carbon dioxide (CO_2) found in the atmosphere. In the over-all course of photosynthesis, six molecules of CO_2 are combined with the addition of hydrogen to give one molecule of carbohydrate ($C_6H_{12}O_6$). The light energy trapped and converted into chemical energy in photosynthesis is available to the plant in the form of the bond energy necessary to hold together the atoms composing the carbohydrate. In reactions taking place in the mitochondria, the cell methodically takes apart the carbohydrate molecule made during photosynthesis and releases the energy present in the bonds.

The over-all process of photosynthesis can be written in chemical terms:

$$6CO_2 + 6H_2O \xrightarrow[\text{CHLOROPHYLL}]{\text{LIGHT}} C_6H_{12}O_6 + 6O_2$$

The reaction can be divided into two parts. The first is the light reaction and is that part in which light and chlorophyll are involved. It is during the light reaction that light energy is converted to chemical energy. This chemical energy is used to synthesize carbohydrate from CO_2 during the second part of photosynthesis, termed the *dark reaction*. The term "dark reaction" does not mean that the reaction occurs only in the dark but that the reactions do not require light. The dark reaction is a series of rather straightforward synthetic reactions similar in outline but different in detail from any number of other synthetic reactions that occur in the cell. The light reaction is the unique stage of photosynthesis.

Chlorophyll and Light Absorption

The first step in photosynthesis is the absorption of light. Light used in photosynthesis is absorbed by chlorophyll. Evidence for this can be obtained by comparing the absorption spectrum of chlorophyll with the action spectrum of photosynthesis. Every pigment has a distinct absorption spectrum, so that when a beam of white light (which consists of all colors) illuminates the pigment, some of the colors are absorbed by the pigment while the remainder are reflected or transmitted. The eye sees the reflected light but not the absorbed light. Consequently chlorophyll appears green because it absorbs all colors except green, which is reflected. For experimental work, it is possible to determine accurately the color of light that is absorbed by chlorophyll and to express the results in a graph in which the amount of light absorbed is plotted against the wavelength of the light used (Fig. 3-8).

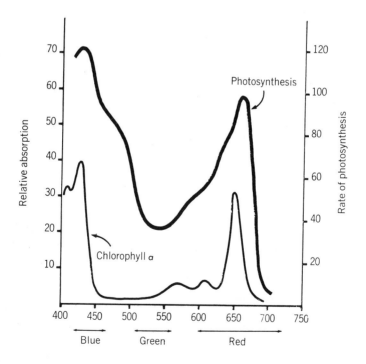

Fig. 3-8. *Absorption spectrum of chlorophyll* a *and the action spectrum for photosynthesis.*

The action spectrum of photosynthesis is found by determining at which wavelengths of light photosynthesis occurs. This can be done in any number of ways. One of the most precise is to shine equal amounts of light of known wavelengths on a suspension of algae and to measure the amount of oxygen released. From the over-all equation for photosynthesis it is clear that the amount of oxygen released is a direct measure of the amount of photosynthesis being carried on. The oxygen liberated can be measured by sensitive electrical means and the data collected can be plotted in a graphic form similar to the absorption data for chlorophyll (Fig. 3-8). This time the amount of photosynthesis is plotted against the wavelength of the light used.

The two spectra are very similar. When absorption spectra are made for other pigments, such as the carotenoids, they show little or no similarity to the action spectrum of photosynthesis.

Both the absorption and the action spectra make the same important point: not all wavelengths of light are used with equal effectiveness in photosynthesis. Blue and red light are the most effective and important.

The Light Reactions of Photosynthesis

When light falls on chlorophyll, the chlorophyll becomes energized for a brief instant; this is termed an *excited* state. The excitation results in the chlorophyll's donating an electron to another molecule. The chlorophyll then returns to its former state by accepting an electron from still another molecule. The over-all effect is that the chlorophyll is an electron pump, pumping electrons from one substance to another.

Ultimately, electrons are pumped from water to CO_2 (Fig. 3-9). An electron from the hydrogen of the water molecule is transferred to a higher energy level where it is trapped by a *pyridine nucleotide* (PN); at the same time, *adenosine triphosphate* (ATP) is formed from adenosine diphosphate (ADP) and inorganic phosphate. These two reactions are of utmost importance in all energy transformations in the cell.

The first reaction, that of moving a pair of electrons from a lower to a higher energy level by means of a pyridine nucleotide, is termed *electron transport*. The structure of the pyridine nucleotide most commonly involved in electron transfer in plants is shown in Fig. 3-10. The energetic electron from the hydrogen of water combines with the pyridine nucleotide and a hydrogen atom lacking an electron (H^+) to produce reduced pyridine nucleotide (PNH_2). The PNH_2 is a compound with considerable energy—energy that can be released by

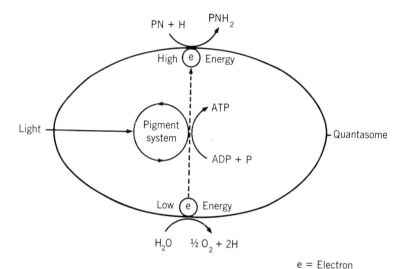

e = Electron

Fig. 3-9. *General concept of the light reactions and associated electron-transport pathways in photosynthesis. From R. Park, "Photosynthetic Reactions of Cells," in* The General Physiology of Cell Specialization, *edited by Mazia and Tyler (McGraw-Hill Book Co., Inc., 1963), by permission.*

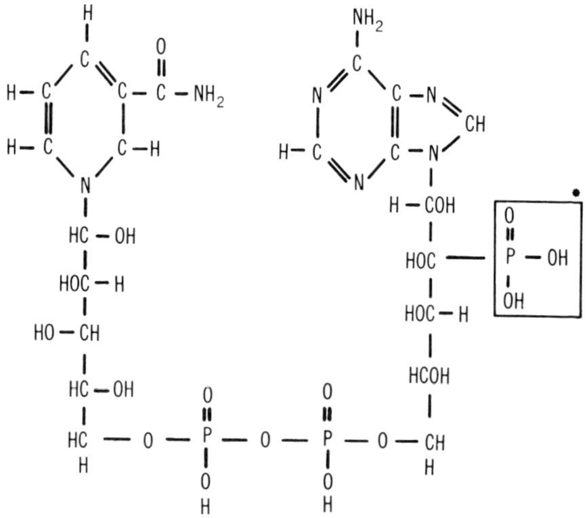

* Removal of the phosphate makes the compound diphosphopyridine nucleotide (DPN).

Fig. 3-10. *Structural formula of triphosphopyridine nucleotide (TPN).*

reversing the reaction. This reverse occurs in the dark-reaction phase of photosynthesis when the energy is used to convert CO_2 into carbohydrate.

The second reaction, the conversion of ADP plus phosphate to ATP, is a consequence of the first. Energy is made available during electron transfer and this energy is used to add the phosphate to ADP. The formula for ADP and ATP is shown in Fig. 3-11. From this figure

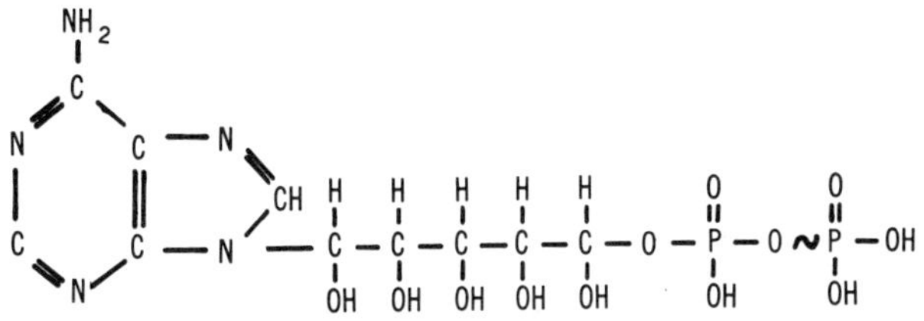

Adenosine diphosphate (ADP)

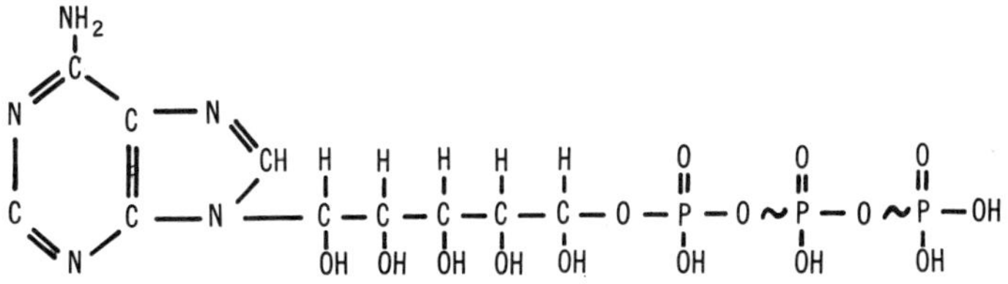

Adenosine triphosphate (ATP)

Fig. 3-11. *Formula for adenosine diphosphate and adenosine triphosphate.*

it is clear that the only difference between the two compounds is an additional phosphate unit in ATP. But this is a highly significant difference, because the phosphate-to-phosphate bond that is produced is different from the usual chemical bond. It is a high-energy bond, which means that the energy involved is considerably greater than that normally found in chemical bonds. This fact is usually noted, when depicting the compound, by using a wavy line in place of a straight line in connecting the phosphates. The energy stored in this phosphate bond can be released by the breakdown of ATP to ADP plus P. The formation and breakdown of ATP is the major means of energy transfer in the cell. In *respiration,* as in photosynthesis, electron transfer is coupled with the formation of ATP, and energy is made available to the cell. The molecules of ATP made available through respiration are used for a large number of reactions, many of them synthetic; the

ATP's made available through the light reactions of photosynthesis are used in the synthesis of carbohydrate from CO_2.

The products of the light reaction, then, are PNH_2 and ATP. The by-product is oxygen, which is released into the atmosphere.

The CO_2-Fixation Cycle

The next phase of photosynthesis involves the conversion of CO_2 to carbohydrate $(C_6H_{12}O_6)$. It might be thought that this would occur through building on one CO_2 molecule after another until a six-carbon molecule is obtained. This is not the case. Instead, a more indirect but characteristic method is used—a cycle in which one unit of CO_2 is handled at a time and the chemicals involved in the cycle are regenerated during the course of the cycle.

The cycle is shown in Fig. 3-12. The entry of CO_2 into the cycle can be seen in the upper right-hand corner. The molecule to which the CO_2 is attached has five carbon atoms and two phosphate groups. It is called *ribulose diphosphate*. The addition of the CO_2 results in the formation of an unstable six-carbon compound, shown in brackets in Fig. 3-11. This compound immediately breaks into two three-carbon compounds, called *phosphoglyceric acid* or PGA. Unlike the six-carbon compounds, PGA is stable and may be considered the first product of the CO_2-fixation phase.

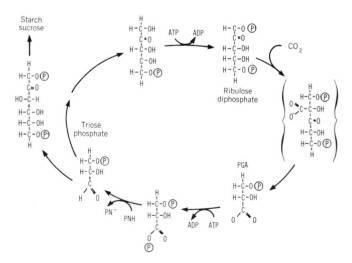

Fig. 3-12. *CO_2 fixation cycle of photosynthesis.*

Thus far, the energy made available from the light reaction has not been utilized. This happens in the next couple of reactions where the energy of the ATP and the PNH_2 is incorporated through the reactions shown in the lower left-hand portion of Fig. 3-12. Through the addition and then loss of a phosphate and the conversion of PNH_2 to PN, an oxygen atom is removed and PGA is converted to the sugar triose phosphate, which is at a higher energy level.

Finally, two triose-phosphate molecules are joined end to end, resulting in a six-carbon sugar with two phosphates. The two phosphates are next removed and $C_6H_{12}O_6$ results.

While these reactions are occurring, additional reactions, starting from triose phosphate, result in the formation of ribulose diphosphate. At this point the cycle takes another turn when CO_2 couples with ribulose diphosphate. Each turn of the cycle actually involves not the few reactions shown in Fig. 3-12 but usually ten to fifteen separate reactions. The entire cycle is driven by the energy available from the light reactions in the form of PNH_2 and ATP.

While the major products of photosynthesis may be considered to be carbohydrates, many other compounds are produced from one or another of the intermediate compounds. Amino acids, which are the basic unit of proteins, as well as fatty acids and glycerol, the basic units of lipids and fats, are also products of photosynthesis.

Chloroplast Structure and Photosynthesis

The chloroplast has an elaborate internal structure clearly visible in Fig. 3-3. What is the relation of this structure to the reactions of photosynthesis?

The lamellae are known to contain the photosynthetic pigments. In addition, it is possible to demonstrate that the light reactions (formation of ATP, PNH_2, and O_2) occur in the lamellar portion of the chloroplast. Recent work has indicated that the lamellae are actually formed of closely packed oblate spheres, which have been given the name *quantasomes* (Fig. 3-13). There is considerable evidence to indicate that each molecule of chlorophyll does not act independently but that several hundred act together to absorb a single unit or quantum of light energy. The quantasome may be the physical manifestation of this group of chlorophyll molecules, which is called the *photosynthetic unit.*

The CO_2-fixation cycle is located not in the lamellar structure but in the amorphous-appearing stroma. Here are located the hundreds of

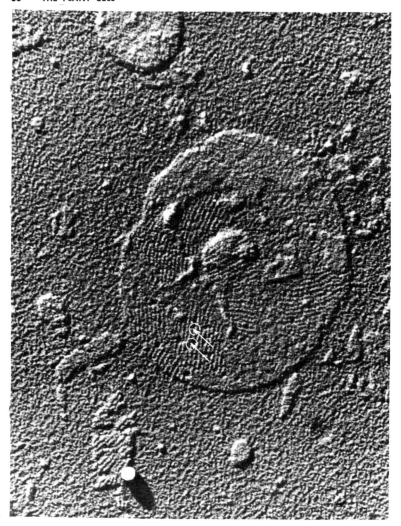

Fig. 3-13. *Lamella of chloroplast showing quantasomes. Courtesy of Dr. P. Healey, U. of California, Berkeley.*

compounds necessary for the fixation of CO_2 and the utilization of the energy made available from the light reaction.

Thus, not only is the process of photosynthesis chemically divided into two parts but these parts are separated within the chloroplast. Much yet remains to be learned concerning photosynthesis, particularly concerning the details of the light reaction and the relation of structure to function on the molecular level, but rapid progress is being made at present and will undoubtedly continue in the future.

Starch and Amyloplasts

The six-carbon sugar formed at the end of photosynthesis may be used directly in metabolism. On the other hand, sucrose may be formed by joining two six-carbon sugars. Sucrose is the form in which most carbohydrate is moved through the plant. Another alternative is to store the product of photosynthesis in the form of starch.

Starch is a major, although far from the sole, carbohydrate food-storage form in the plant. On the molecular level, starch consists of long chains of glucose molecules in the form of a helix (Fig. 3-14). Cellulose also consists of long chains of glucose molecules, but the manner in which the molecules are joined together is not the same. This results in different physical properties and functions of the two molecules in the plant.

The formation of starch may take place in the chloroplast itself. In

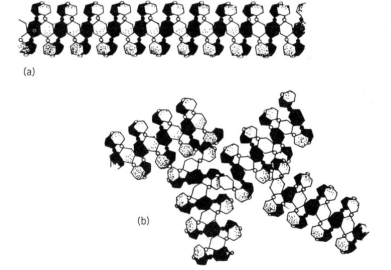

(a)

(b)

Fig. 3-14. *Molecular structure of starch. (a) Unbranched form (amylose). (b) Branched form (amylopectin). From Bonner and Galston,* Principles of Plant Physiology *(W. H. Freeman & Co., 1952), by permission.*

the algae this is the usual case and the starch is associated with a special structure—the *pyrenoid*. The chloroplasts of the ferns and seed plants lack pyrenoids and, although there are exceptions, usually do not form large amounts of starch. In these plants the mass of starch is stored in special colorless plastids called *amyloplasts,* in which are found the enzymes necessary for the formation of starch. The starch is deposited in layers; one layer is laid down on top of the previous one until a large starch grain is formed.

The amyloplasts are not the only type of storage plastid. Another type is involved in the storage of protein; it is found in the seeds of many plants and is a ready source of amino acids to the cells during periods of rapid growth associated with germination. Still another plastid in this same group is known to store oils. Fats and oils are even better energy sources than the carbohydrates and are frequently found as reserve energy supplies in both plant and animal cells.

THE ORIGIN AND DEVELOPMENT OF PLASTIDS

In some algae and mosses, chloroplasts can be seen to divide (Fig. 3-15). The chloroplasts of the ferns and seed plants have not been observed to divide and the mode of their origin has long been controversial. There is evidence, although not conclusive, that in the seed plants the chloroplasts are self-perpetuating bodies even though they have not been seen to divide. They may arise from smaller bodies, usually termed *proplastids,* as shown in Fig. 3-16.

When these proplastids develop in the light the lamellae are formed through the fusion of vesicles produced by invaginations of the inner layer of the double membrane surrounding the chloroplast. In the

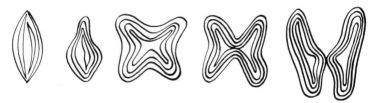

Fig. 3-15. *Division of a chloroplast in a brown alga (Fucus). From Diter von Wittstein, "Developmental Changes in Chloroplasts and Their Genetic Control," in* Developmental Cytology, *edited by Dorothea Rudnick. Copyright © 1959, The Ronald Press Company. By permission.*

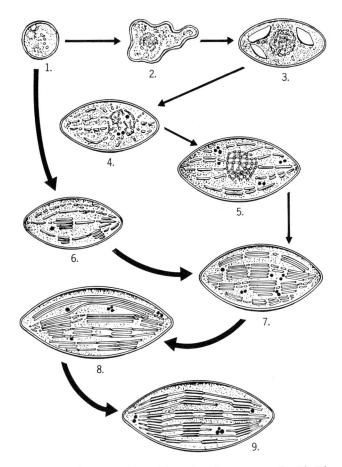

Fig. 3-16. *Development of a chloroplast from a proplastid. The stages connected by the bold arrows occur in plants grown in the light. The stages connected by the light arrows occur in plants grown in the dark. These plants, when placed in the light, are converted from stage 5 to stage 7. From von Wittstein, in* Developmental Cytology. *Copyright © 1959, The Ronald Press Company. By permission.*

dark, tubular structures are formed which are arranged in a lattice. When the chloroplast is placed in the light, this lattice becomes rearranged in the form of the usual lamellar structure found in the mature chloroplast.

Environmental conditions other than light also influence plastid development. Such factors as mineral nutrition and temperature can determine the course and rate of plastid growth. Plastid development is also under the control of the genes which, as the inheritable units of the cell, ultimately determine the development of the organism. As will be discussed later, the genes are usually considered to be located in the nucleus and are part of the chromosomes. In the case of chloroplasts, however, the matter of genetic control of development is complicated by the presence of inheritable units in the plastids themselves as well as in the nucleus. Thus, while some features of plastid development are controlled by the nuclear genes, others are under the control of genes located on the plastids. Because the current concepts of genes are based on the structure of DNA, the presence of DNA in the chloroplasts of nonvascular and vascular plants has been repeatedly sought. While few cases of DNA occurring in chloroplasts have been reported, many workers believe DNA will be found in plastids. Clearly, large amounts of RNA are present, a fact that should be kept in mind during the later discussion of RNA and protein synthesis (Chapter 6).

4

RESPIRATION

AND

MITOCHONDRIA

THE RELEASE OF ENERGY

Photosynthesis results in the conversion of light energy to chemical energy. This chemical energy is incorporated into the bonds of synthesized compounds, primarily six-carbon sugars. The energy present in such compounds is essentially stored energy, which can be released only by breaking the chemical bonds that hold the molecule together.

The energy present may be released by breaking all the bonds at the same time. This type of energy release occurs when a piece of wood burns. An indication of the amount of energy involved is given by the heat and light evolved during the combustion. Biological systems effect the release of energy in a similar yet far more subtle way. Each bond may be broken individually, and the released energy is then trapped by suitable receptors in ways that permit the future transfer of this energy to other compounds.

The receptors of the released energy are the same as those involved in energy transformations in photosynthesis: ADP and PN. The energy-rich compounds that result are also the same as in photosynthesis: ATP and PNH_2. These compounds are extremely important to the cell. They are the negotiable energy currency of the cell, the currency that must be available for investment in the building and maintenance of the cell.

The systematic breakdown of a molecule such as glucose is a complex undertaking, and in the cell it is accomplished by scores of reactions. Each of these reactions is controlled by a specific enzyme, and the entire process involves many enzymes acting in teams.

43

ENZYMES

Enzymes have been termed organic catalysts and this is an accurate, if limited, statement. A catalyst can be defined as a compound that speeds up a chemical reaction and yet remains unchanged at the end of the reaction. In the case of the enzyme *amylase,* the reaction that is catalyzed is the breakdown of starch to individual glucose molecules. Some breakdown would occur, if enough time were available, without the presence of amylase. But in the presence of amylase the reaction is rapid and large amounts of glucose appear. Amylase does not change the course of the reaction. Moreover, although amylase is involved in the reaction, it is unchanged at the end of the reaction.

Enzymes lower the activation energy of reactions in which they are involved. Molecules will break down if their energy is increased to a point where the molecules are no longer stable. The energy needed to achieve this point is called the *energy of activation.* As the temperature is raised and more energy is available, the reaction rate increases. Enzymes, by lowering the activation energy of the reaction (Fig.4-1),

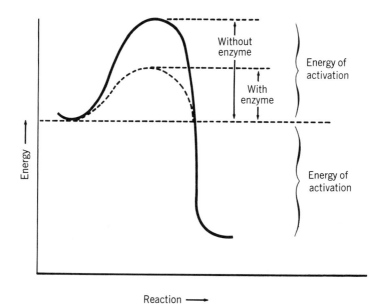

Fig. 4-1. *Energy of activation for a chemical reaction with and without the presence of an enzyme.*

permit reactions to occur at normal environmental temperatures. How enzymes are able to permit such reactions is unknown.

All enzymes are proteins. They are, with few exceptions, large molecules composed of hundreds of amino acids. The amino acids are joined together in long, elaborately coiled chains. Some enzymes consist solely of proteins, while many consist of two parts. The larger of these two parts is inevitably a protein molecule. This does not mean that all proteins are enzymes; but a part of every enzyme is a protein. The second part, called the co-enzyme, may be a metal such as iron, manganese, or copper, or a vitamin such as thiamin, riboflavin, or nicotinic acid. When an enzyme consists of two parts, both parts must be present for the enzyme to function. The fact that enzymes are proteins and therefore highly complex molecules means that most enzymes are easily damaged. Any treatment that will break down or alter (denature) proteins will destroy the enzymes' activity. Thus, while an increase in temperature will increase the rate of an enzymatic reaction, too high a temperature denatures the protein and the enzymatic reaction ceases. Any number of other changes in the immediate environment of the enzyme molecule may result in the loss of activity.

The enzyme molecule is believed to combine with the substrate molecule (Fig. 4-2). This combination is short-lived and, when it breaks up, the enzyme molecule remains intact while the substrate molecule is changed. Enzymes are highly specific. This specificity is believed to be based on the spatial configuration of the surface of the enzyme molecule. Enzymes can be inhibited by compounds that closely resemble the substrate but that are inactive in the reaction. A well-known and important example of this type of enzyme inhibition involves the enzyme *succinic dehydrogenase,* which acts on the substrate succinic acid. Another compound, *malonic acid,* closely resembles succinic acid but is different enough so that the enzyme while combining with the malonic acid does not change it. The malonic acid, however, occupies the reactive site on the enzyme molecule and prohibits the attachment of succinic acid. This type of inhibition is termed *competitive inhibition.* Other types of enzyme inhibitors act by combining or changing various parts of the enzyme molecule so that the reactive site is destroyed. A large number of enzyme inhibitors have been discovered and their use has led to the elucidation of many aspects of enzyme action.

Each enzyme mediates only a limited number of reactions—in most cases, only one. Thus, an enzyme involved in a reaction that results in the loss of a hydrogen atom from one compound is different from an

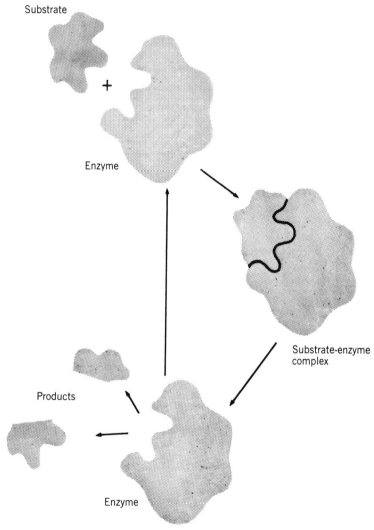

Substrate

+

Enzyme

Substrate-enzyme
complex

Products

Enzyme

Fig. 4-2. *Diagrammatic representation of the enzyme-substrate complex and the enzyme reaction.*

enzyme involved in a similar type of reaction with a different compound. Consequently, there are hundreds of enzymes in the cell, each acting on a specific compound or substrate. To understand the functioning and growth of a cell, we must understand the factors controlling enzyme formation.

A formidable body of information indicates that enzyme synthesis is controlled by genes. Many of the details of the nature and method of this control are now understood and will be discussed later.

A feature of many enzymes is that they function in teams. In such an arrangement, the end product of one enzymatic reaction becomes the substrate for the next enzyme in the series. This pattern can be repeated dozens of times. The CO_2-fixation cycle discussed in relation to photosynthesis is an example of enzymes working in a team. Similar arrangements of enzymes are found in the breakdown or respiration of carbohydrates.

RESPIRATION

Respiration is the biologically controlled breakdown of energy-containing substances, such as carbohydrates, fats, and proteins, with the release of energy. As such, it is the reverse of photosynthesis, in which energy is used to synthesize compounds. The major pathway of respiration in the cell can be broken into two parts: (1) *glycolysis* and (2) the *Krebs cycle.* In the first part, glycolysis, glucose is eventually split into two pyruvic acid molecules, each having three carbon atoms. At this point, the second part of respiration begins; and after one carbon is removed, the remaining two-carbon compound enters the Krebs cycle. During the Krebs cycle, the two-carbon compound is converted to CO_2. This part of respiration is a cycle because the reactions are organized so that the chemical compound *oxalacetic acid,* which accepts the two-carbon piece entering the cycle, is regenerated at the end of the cycle and can accept another two-carbon piece.

The two parts of respiration differ in a number of important features. In the absence of oxygen, glycolysis can occur but the Krebs cycle cannot function. If no oxygen is present, the pyruvic acid produced at the end of glycolysis is converted, with the loss of one carbon atom, to ethyl alcohol. In this case, the process is *fermentation.*

Another important difference between glycolysis and the Krebs cycle is the amount of energy made available to the plant cell in the form of ATP molecules. The important consideration is not the total number of ATP molecules formed but the net number available at the end of the reactions. This is because some energy in the form of ATP must be invested if the reactions are to occur. During glycolysis, only two ATP molecules are obtained per glucose molecule respired, while in the Krebs cycle the net gain is 38 ATP molecules per glucose molecule.

Anaerobic Respiration

$$C_6H_{12}O_6 \longrightarrow 2C_2H_6O + 2CO_2$$

This equation is the over-all reaction for fermentation. It states merely that one molecule of glucose is converted to two molecules of ethyl alcohol and two molecules of carbon dioxide. This is the merest outline of the reactions involved. These reactions are indicated more fully in Fig. 4-3, which shows a minimum of some ten steps between glucose and ethyl alcohol.

The first step in fermentation is the addition of a phosphate to the glucose molecule. Shortly after, a second phosphate is added. These steps are carried out at the expense of two ATP molecules. The end product is a six-carbon sugar with two phosphates attached, called *fructose-1, 6-diphosphate.* This is split into two three-carbon compounds and, in the reactions that follow, two ATP molecules as well as two PNH_2 molecules are generated—one each per three-carbon compound. As the reactions continue, pyruvic acid is produced, which results in the formation of an additional ATP per three-carbon fragment. Finally, as a necessary consequence of the absence of oxygen, the electrons from the PNH_2's are used to produce ethyl alcohol. This final reaction results in the formation of one CO_2 per pyruvic acid molecule.

If a balance sheet is compiled to show the energy of the compounds involved, it will show that, for each glucose molecule used, four ATP molecules and two PNH_2 molecules are produced at the expense of two ATP molecules and two PNH_2 molecules. The net gain is thus two ATP's. There is considerable energy remaining in the ethyl alcohol— energy that can be released only by different metabolic pathways.

The basic reactions involved in anaerobic respiration are diagrammed in Fig. 4-4, which shows only the fate of the carbon atoms and the net changes in ATP. The first stages of anaerobic respiration are very similar to part of the CO_2-fixation cycle of photosynthesis, discussed in Chapter 3. The direction of the reactions is reversed in the two processes. Except for this and differences in the details of the steps, the reactions from fructose-1, 6-diphosphate to PGA are essentially the same.

The entire process of fermentation can be carried out in the complete absence of oxygen. Fermentation is the major energy-producing system of many micro-organisms. Commercially, the most important of these organisms are the yeasts. The production of alcohol through fermentation has been discovered by almost every civilization, and the art of making alcoholic beverages has been practiced for centuries.

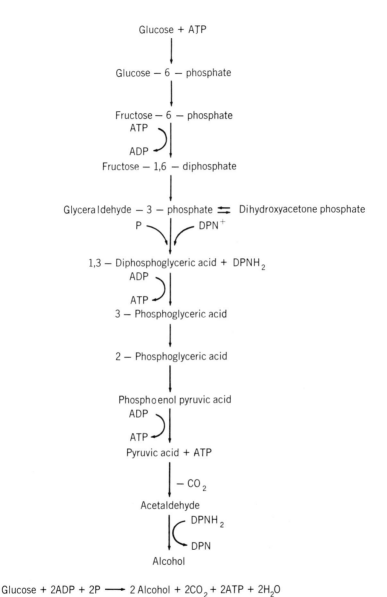

Glucose + ATP

Glucose − 6 − phosphate

Fructose − 6 − phosphate

ATP
ADP

Fructose − 1,6 − diphosphate

Glyceraldehyde − 3 − phosphate ⇌ Dihydroxyacetone phosphate

P DPN^+

1,3 − Diphosphoglyceric acid + $DPNH_2$

ADP
ATP

3 − Phosphoglyceric acid

2 − Phosphoglyceric acid

Phosphoenol pyruvic acid

ADP
ATP

Pyruvic acid + ATP

$− CO_2$

Acetaldehyde

$DPNH_2$
DPN

Alcohol

Glucose + 2ADP + 2P ⟶ 2 Alcohol + $2CO_2$ + 2ATP + $2H_2O$

Fig. 4-3. *Summary of the chemical reactions involved in fermentation.*

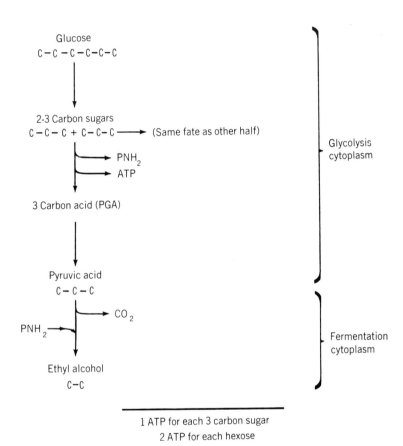

Fig. 4-4. *Summary diagram (omitting many of the intermediate steps) of anaerobic respiration.*

Aerobic Respiration

$$C_6H_{12}O_2 + O_2 \longrightarrow 6CO_2 + 6H_2O$$

In the presence of oxygen and the necessary enzymes, the breakdown of glucose is complete and occurs as outlined in the equation above. For every molecule of glucose used, six molecules of CO_2 and six molecules of H_2O are produced. During the course of this reaction there is a net production of 38 ATP molecules produced and made available to the plant.

Aerobic respiration, as noted earlier, can be described as having two parts. During the first part, the glucose molecule becomes involved in a set of reactions that yields two pyruvic-acid molecules. This part is identical to the similar reactions that occur in anaerobic respiration. At this point, however, the fate of the pyruvic acid differs depending on the presence or absence of oxygen and the appropriate enzymes.

In the presence of oxygen, a carbon atom is removed from the pyruvic acid and an activated two-carbon compound is formed. This compound unites with a four-carbon compound, *oxalacetic acid,* form-

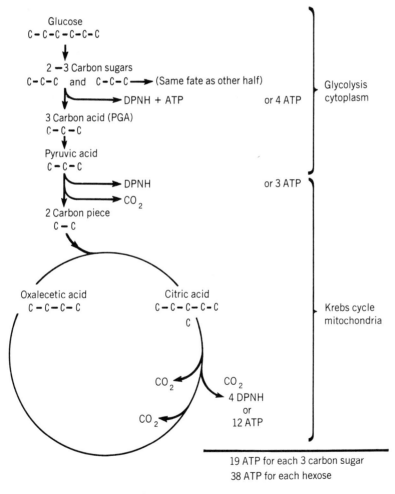

Fig. 4-5. *Summary diagram of glycolysis and the Krebs cycle.*

ing citric acid, which contains six carbon atoms. Then, through a series of reactions shown in Fig. 4-5, two CO_2 molecules are released and oxalacetic acid is formed. For each CO_2 molecule produced, six ATP molecules are made, so that, for each two-carbon fragment entering the cycle, 12 ATP molecules are made available to the cell.

The total energy relations in aerobic respiration are more involved. The aerobic cell receives more energy from the first part of respiration than does the yeast cell for the same series of reactions. This results from the fact that in the yeast cell the PNH_2 that is produced is used later in the formation of alcohol. In the aerobic cell, the energy of this PNH_2 is converted to three ATP molecules. Thus the net gain of ATP in the yeast is two ATP molecules, while in the aerobic cell it is eight ATP molecules per glucose molecule. An additional six ATP molecules are gained between pyruvic acid and the Krebs cycle. The total number of ATP molecules produced per glucose molecule used is 38 (8 + 6 + 24 = 38). Aerobic respiration is thus a much more efficient process with regard to energy release than is fermentation.

Direct Oxidation Pathway

The major pathway of aerobic respiration appears to be through glycolysis and the Krebs cycle. Another pathway, known as the *direct oxidation pathway* or the *pentose phosphate shunt mechanism,* is known to exist in both plants and animals. More involved in some ways than the glycolysis-Krebs-cycle reactions, it has the same over-all equation:

$$C_6H_{12}O_6 + 6O_2 \longrightarrow 6CO_2 + 6H_2O$$

The first steps are the same as in glycolysis, but one CO_2 and a five-carbon sugar are then formed. This sugar is broken down through a rather complex set of reactions involving a number of three-, six-, and seven-carbon compounds. Ultimately, for every six glucose molecules entering the cycle, six five-carbon sugars, six CO_2 molecules, and 12 PNH_2 molecules are produced. The energy of the PNH_2 can be converted to 36 ATP molecules. The reaction is, therefore, nearly as efficient as the glycolysis-Krebs-cycle pathway. The five-carbon sugars produced are important in the synthesis of ATP and various other cellular constituents. Moreover, these same reactions play a very important role in the CO_2-fixation cycle of photosynthesis.

Electron Transfer and Oxygen Uptake

The presence of oxygen is necessary for aerobic respiration to take place. The uptake of oxygen during respiration is a consequence of the transfer to oxygen of electrons from the various compounds involved in the metabolic breakdown of glucose. This transfer of electrons results in a reduction of oxygen gas to water. The fact that electrons have varying amounts of energy was stressed in the discussion of photosynthesis. During photosynthesis, electrons are raised to higher energy levels and their energy is ultimately incorporated into the bonds of carbohydrate molecules. During respiration, electrons pass through a series of reactions that take them from high energy levels to lower energy levels. At the lowest level, the electron combines with oxygen and H^+ ions to form water. At the intermediate levels, the energy re-

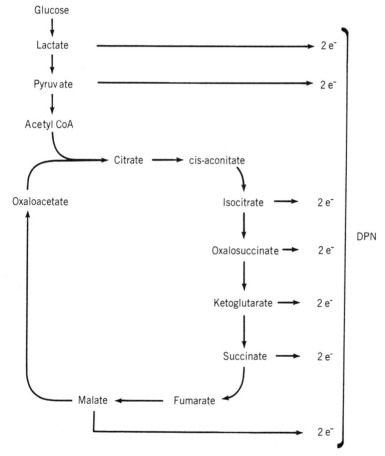

Fig. 4-6. *Steps at which electrons are removed during the glycolysis-Krebs cycle pathway.*

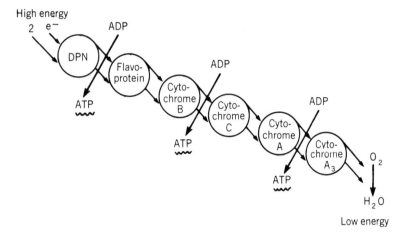

Fig. 4-7. *Electron-transfer reactions.*

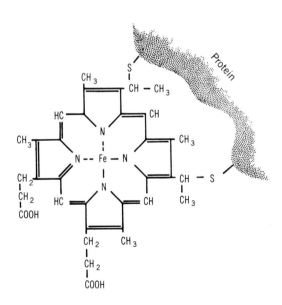

Fig. 4-8. *Molecular structure of cytochrome.*

leased is transformed into high-energy phosphate bonds by the conversion of ADP to ATP.

At six places in the glycolysis-Krebs-cycle pathway, a pair of electrons is released (Fig. 4-6). These electrons are accepted by PN, which becomes PNH_2. Then, through a series of cyclic reactions shown in Fig. 4-7, the electrons move down a series of compounds. During this passage, the electrons lose energy and ATP molecules are formed. The compounds involved in these reactions are PN, a *flavoprotein,* and a series of *cytochromes.* The latter contain iron and have the general structure shown in Fig. 4-8. The final step in the electron-transfer system is the reduction of O_2 to water mediated by the enzyme *cytochrome oxidase.*

The Metabolism of Fats and Proteins

This discussion has stressed the metabolism of carbohydrates, and glucose in particular; however, most of the compounds present in the cell can be respired. Most types of carbohydrates can be and are used. Similarly, fats and proteins may also be respired.

Both fats and proteins can undergo a series of reactions that eventually reduce them to two-carbon fragments, which can enter the Krebs cycle. The utilization of fats and oils supplies much of the energy used during germination. Fats are a highly efficient means of storing energy, since on a comparative-weight basis they have more stored energy than the carbohydrates.

Proteins can be utilized as an energy source, but they are not normally used in this manner. In general, only after other energy sources are exhausted are the proteins respired.

Site of Respiration in the Cell

The fact that the chloroplasts were the site of photosynthesis in the cell was known long before the process was understood. Conversely, the mechanism of respiration was known in considerable detail before the site of the process was determined in the cell.

The major breakthrough in the search for the site of respiration in the cell came with the development of the methods of cell homogenization and separation of cell parts by differential centrifugation. During differential centrifugation, the solution containing the cell parts is rotated rapidly at varying speeds. The parts separate because the heavier parts settle to the bottom of the tube first and then the lighter ones follow. When the cell parts are separated and the oxygen uptake is measured as an indication of respiration, the results obtained are similar to

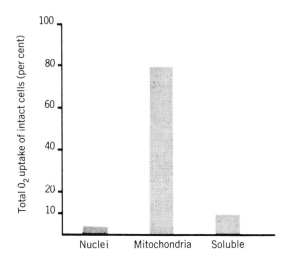

Fig. 4-9. *Amount of oxygen uptake by various cell parts.*

those shown in Fig. 4-9. From studies like these and from other lines of evidence, it has been established that the enzymes of the Krebs cycle are found associated with the mitochondria. The enzymes of glycolysis, on the other hand, are found primarily (although not exclusively) in the soluble portion of the cytoplasm.

The localization of the enzymes of the Krebs cycle in the mitochondria was one of the first and greatest discoveries using cell fractionation procedures.

MITOCHONDRIA

The mitochondria were first seen in cells by the great German cytologist R. Altmann about 1900. In the light microscope, they appear as small spheres, rods, or filaments. They vary in size but are generally 0.5 to 1.0 μ in diameter and 1 to 2 μ in length (Fig. 4-10a). Their small size makes them difficult to observe in the light microscope, and nothing can be seen of their internal structure. Through the use of thin-sectioning techniques and the electron microscope, however, mitochondria can be observed to have a rather elaborate internal structure (Fig. 4-10b; for additional examples see Fig. 5-1). The mitochondria consist of both an outer and an inner membrane. The inner membrane is folded into the center cavity or matrix of the mitochon-

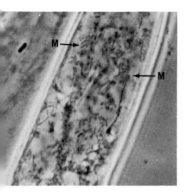 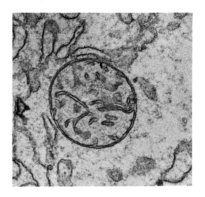

Fig. 4-10. *Structure of the mitochondria as seen in the light microscope (left) and the electron microscope (right).*

drion to form *cristae*. The cristae may be in the form of shelves or in the form of tubular projections. The latter form appears to be more common in plants. The number of cristae frequently is an indication of the amount of respiration occurring. The greater the number of cristae, the greater the oxygen uptake.

Each membrane is a unit membrane and is composed of protein and lipids. There have been reports of the presence of RNA in mitochondria, as well as suggestions that small amounts of DNA may be present.

The origin of mitochondria is a matter of considerable conjecture. They are known to divide in some organisms, but their size in the vast majority of cells would make the occurrence of such an action difficult to discover. They are also believed by some to develop from small undifferentiated structures or *promitochondria*. Other workers believe that they arise from the cell membrane, while still others postulate the nuclear envelope as their site of origin. The one point that seems clear is the need for more research.

MITOCHONDRIAL STRUCTURE AND ENZYME LOCALIZATION

When the internal structure is seen in an electron photomicrograph, the question immediately arises concerning the localization of the enzymes and processes on this level. Recent work has shed considerable light on this problem. The major experimental approach, pioneered by David Green at the University of Wisconsin, has been to break the mitochondria into parts and to analyze each of these parts separately.

Evidence from this type of experiment indicates that the enzymes of the Krebs cycle are located in the region between the membranes, and that the electron-transfer system is found in the membranes themselves (Fig. 4-11). This pattern is not unlike that observed in the

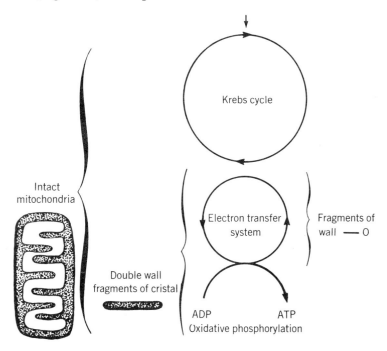

Fig. 4-11. *Possible relation of the parts of the mitochondria to the function of the mitochondria in respiration.*

chloroplast, where the components necessary for the dark reaction, which involves electron transfer, is associated with the lamella and the CO_2 fixation cycle with the stroma.

Recently, mitochondria have been shown to have stalked particles on the surface of their membranes. These particles have been seen in special electron-microscope preparations of mitochondria in animal cells (Fig. 4-12). They consist of a hollow stem 30 to 35 A wide and 45 to 50 A long and have a spherical head 75 to 80 A in diameter. They are spaced at roughly 100 A intervals along the membrane. While the function of these particles is unknown, they do not appear

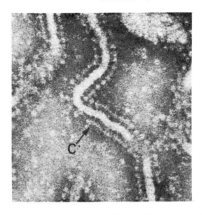

Fig. 4-12. *Particles on the cristae (C) of liver mitochondria in an electron-microscope preparation. In this type of preparation, called "negative staining," the membranes appear light and the background dark. From Donald F. Parsons, "Mitochondrial Structure: Two Types of Subunits on Negatively Stained Mitochondrial Membranes," Science, Vol. 140 (31 May 1963), pp. 985–987, Fig. 1, p. 985. By permission.*

to be the electron-transport particles and may contain the enzymes of oxidative phosphorylation.

Recent research on the localization of enzyme systems in relation to the ultrastructure of both mitochondria and chloroplasts emphasizes again the importance of the interrelation of form and function on all levels of the organism. On the molecular, subcellular, cellular, or whole-organism level, form and function interlock and permit life to exist.

5

GOLGI BODIES,

LYSOSOMES,

AND SPHEROSOMES

THE GOLGI BODIES OR DICTYOSOMES

The plastids and the mitochondria are not the only cytoplasmic particles present in the cell, although at present they are the best understood. Among the cell parts that are present in the cytoplasm are the Golgi bodies or dictyosomes. They derive their name from Camillio Golgi, an Italian cytologist working at the turn of the present century. He described particular staining bodies in nerve cells. The true nature and existence of these bodies was a matter of scientific controversy that lasted for nearly fifty years. Some cytologists believed they could be seen in microscopic preparations while others were equally certain they could not. Only observations made with the electron microscope proved the universal existence of Golgi bodies in both plant and animal cells.

The appearance of a Golgi body in the electron microscope is shown in Fig. 5-1. A three-dimensional diagram of the typical Golgi body found in a plant cell is shown in Fig. 5-2. The center of the Golgi body is composed of a series of discs. Each disc is composed of a double membrane. Around the edges of the discs are rows of small vesicles, which may be derived from the central discs. There are variations of this general pattern both in the size and number of the discs and of the vesicles. In at least one case, such changes in the structure of the Golgi bodies can be correlated with the development of the cell. In the root cap cells, which surround the tip of the root, the young cells have Golgi bodies similar to the one shown in Fig. 5-1. As a cell becomes older, it develops a special thick cell wall. During the growth

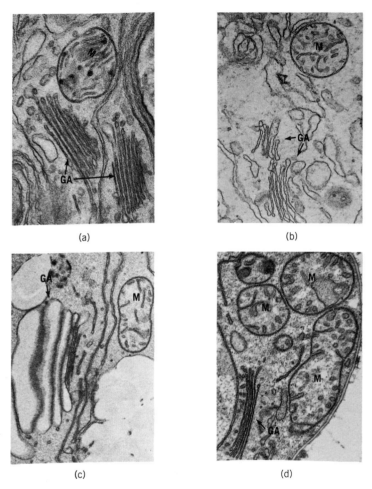

Fig. 5-1. *Electron-microscope photographs of a Golgi body (GA) in different types of cells. M: mitochondria. (a) Pollen type. (b) Nucellar cell. (c) Root cap cell (courtesy of Dr. H. Mollenhauer, U. of Texas). (d) Fungal cell (courtesy of Dr. M. S. Fuller, U. of California, Berkeley).*

of this wall, the Golgi bodies expand and produce large vesicles, which appear to contain material similar to that found in the wall (Fig. 5-3). These vesicles apparently migrate to the surface of the cell and discharge their contents, which fuse with the other wall materials. In this way, the Golgi bodies appear to play a role in the synthesis of wall

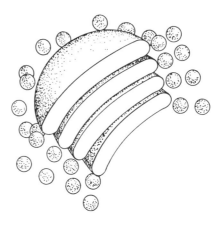

Fig. 5-2. *Three-dimensional drawing of a Golgi body.*

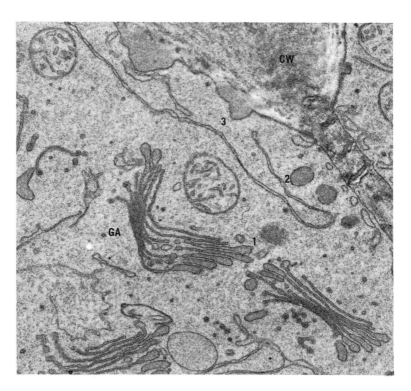

Fig. 5-3. *Electron-microscope photograph of a Golgi body (GA) active in the production of wall material. (1) Vesicles are produced at margin of Golgi body; (2) vesicles migrate to wall; (3) material of vesicles fuses with wall (CW).*

material. They may also be involved in the formation of the new wall that develops when plant cells divide.

In general, the Golgi bodies are believed to be the site of synthetic activity, although the nature and full extent of this activity is not yet known. The Golgi bodies have proved extremely difficult to work with using the usual biochemical procedures, and new methods will probably have to be developed to study them.

The origin of the Golgi bodies is obscure. There is some evidence that they may divide; but that they arise by division or solely by the division of existing Golgi bodies has not been demonstrated conclusively.

THE LYSOSOMES

The lysosomes constitute another cell part that is elusive and difficult to study. The source of these difficulties is completely different from that of the Golgi bodies. The existence of this cell part was not even suspected until a few years ago, and the best evidence for the existence of lysosomes comes from research on animal cells.

The existence of lysosomes was first indicated in experiments with isolated mitochondria. As described in Chapter 4, mitochondria can

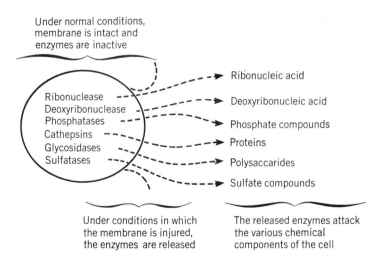

Fig. 5-4. *Diagram of the lysosome concept.*

be isolated from a cell and purified. Attempts to obtain completely pure and uniform mitochondria resulted in the discovery that particles of the same size and shape as mitochondria but containing different enzymes were present. These different enzymes are primarily types that mediate the breakdown of various cell constituents.

The lysosomes have an internal structure different from that of the mitochondria, although they have the same general external form and size. They have a single external membrane and lack internal structure. The current concept of lysosome function is based on the belief that the enzymes present within them remain inactive until the limiting membrane is broken or damaged in such a way that the enzymes are released (Fig. 5-4). The enzymes then become active and the result is the breakdown of the cell. While this may seem unnecessarily destructive, the death and replacement of cells is very important in animals and the breakdown of the cell contents is a regular feature of maturation of many plant cells, particularly vascular cells.

The existence of lysosomes in plant cells has not been demonstrated conclusively. Particles having the same form as the lysosomes of animals can be seen in electron-microscope photographs of plant cells. Also, recent evidence indicates that some of the same enzymes may be present in these particles as are found in animal lysosomes.

THE SPHEROSOMES

When living plant cells are examined in the microscope, the cytoplasm appears to circulate at a rapid rate. The mitochondria, chloroplasts, and other cell parts can be observed to move about in the cell. With careful observation, small, completely spherical particles can be seen moving rapidly through the cell. These are the spherosomes (Fig. 5-5).

Spherosomes are difficult to study because of their small size and their poor preservation in killed and fixed cells. Recently, however, a group of Swiss botanists in the laboratory of Professor Frey-Wyssling have studied the origin and development of spherosomes. They believe that spherosomes are formed by the *endoplasmic reticulum,* which is discussed in the next chapter. Small, immature spherosomes are pinched off from the tube-like endoplasmic reticulum; these spherosomes enlarge, and they result in the type of spherosomes found in many cells. Frequently, enlargement continues and a fat body develops. This development may indicate that the spherosomes are a

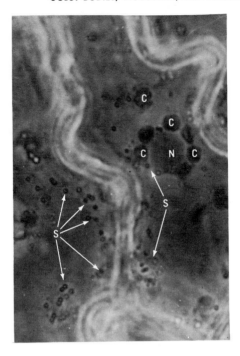

Fig. 5-5. *Phase photomicrograph of spherosomes (S). N: nucleus; C: chloroplasts. Courtesy of Dr. Helen Sorokin.*

special cell part involved in fat production. Many other possible functions have been proposed for spherosomes, and their true function is by no means certain. They are bounded by a single unit membrane. Clearly, much more research will be done in the future on the nature and function of spherosomes and their role in cell metabolism.

6

THE ENDOPLASMIC

RETICULUM,

RIBOSOMES, AND

PROTEIN SYNTHESIS

THE MEMBRANE SYSTEMS OF THE CELL

For many years, the cytoplasm of the living cell was conceived of as a rather homogeneous gel in which particles such as the plastids and the mitochondria were suspended. The electron microscope revealed the existence of additional structures in the cytoplasm and clearly established the complex nature of the cytoplasm. Among the first structures observed with the electron microscope were the *endoplasmic reticulum,* or ER, and the *ribosomes.*

The ER is a system of membranes that permeates the cytoplasm. Although the form of the ER varies greatly, it can most easily be visualized as a deflated inner tube. When sectioned and observed in the electron microscope, it appears as a series of parallel pairs of unit or single membranes (Fig. 6-1). These membranes form an elaborate branching network or reticulum. Sometimes the ER may be in the shape of narrow tubes, but the more common type consists of long, folded sheets of membranes. There appears to be a definite inside and outside to the ER.

Electron-microscope photographs also show that the nucleus is surrounded by a double membrane (Fig. 6-1) having extensive cytoplasmic projections that are continuous with the ER. There is considerable evidence that the nuclear membrane and the ER form a single system in many cells (Fig. 6-2). The relationship of the ER to the cell membrane and the vacuolar membrane is not so clear. Some

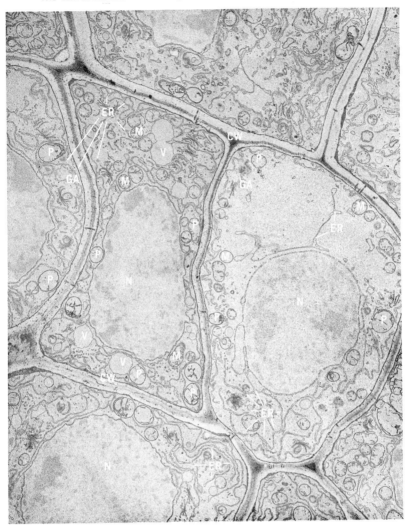

Fig. 6-1. *Electron-microscope photograph of the cytoplasm showing the endoplasmic reticulum.*

cytologists believe that the ER is essentially an infolding of the cell membrane. Some feel that the membrane surrounding the vacuole is continuous with the ER. Both views are not universally shared by cytologists, and only additional information will clarify these relationships.

In any discussion of the membrane systems of the plant cell, par-

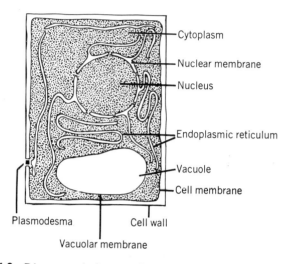

Fig. 6-2. *Diagram of the membrane systems of the plant cell.*

ticularly with regard to the form of the ER, it is important to remember that the cytoplasm is capable of rapid streaming. This streaming of the cytoplasm, or *cyclosis,* is most spectacular in highly vacuolate cells. The cytoplasm and the cytoplasmic particles move at considerable speeds and in rather elaborate patterns. Not all plant cells are believed to show cytoplasmic streaming, although the majority probably do. The mechanism responsible for the streaming is not understood. That energy in the form of ATP is required is known. How streaming may affect the form of the ER is unknown, but the possibility that it may should be remembered.

The amount of ER found in a cell may vary greatly. Factors that influence the amount of ER include external conditions as well as the age and function of the cell. As a rule, resting cells have little ER, while actively growing cells have large amounts. Cells with apparent roles in the nutrition of other cells, such as the vegetative cells surrounding the embryo in the developing seed, have large amounts of ER. On the other hand, mature cells frequently contain only small amounts of ER. Damage to a cell may result in a considerable increase in ER.

The role of the ER in the metabolism of the cell is not clearly understood. One role—as the site of the ribosomes, which function in protein synthesis—is discussed below. As important as this role is, it is only one of the many possible functions. Electron-microscope studies have shown some evidence that the ER forms a transport and storage system, particularly for proteins, within the cell. A role for the ER in the formation of the wall has been suggested on the basis of the frequent close association of the ER and the plasma membrane. Many electron microscopists believe that the ER connects one cell to the next through cytoplasmic strands, called *plasmodesmata,* in the wall (Fig. 6-3). Thus, the ER may be involved in a wide range of cellular activities of considerable importance. As interesting as many of these ideas are, few are well-documented by facts and fewer still are accepted by the majority of plant cytologists.

THE ER AND THE RIBOSOMES

When the ER of tissue fixed with osmium tetroxide is observed with the electron microscope (Fig. 6-4), one side frequently appears rough

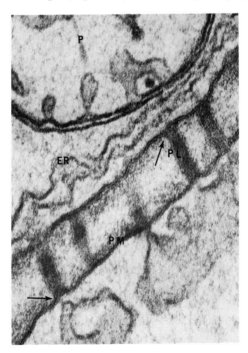

Fig. 6-3. *Plasmodesmata as seen in the electron microscope. PL: plasmodesmata; PM: plasma membrane; ER: endoplasmic reticulum; P: plastid. Arrows indicate places where the plasma membrane is continuous with the plasmodesmata. Note unit-membrane structure of PM.*

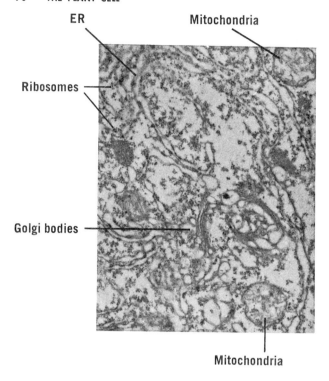

ER   Mitochondria

Ribosomes

Golgi bodies

Mitochondria

Fig. 6-4. *Endoplasmic reticulum and ribosomes as seen in plant tissue fixed in osmium tetroxide.*

as a result of the presence of small, hemispherically shaped bodies approximately 250 A in diameter. These are the *ribosomes*. They may also be free in the cytoplasm, and they can be observed in the nucleus. When the ribosomes are associated with the ER, they are found only on the outside.

Some ER—the smooth type found in many animal cells—has no ribosomes associated with it. How much of the ER has ribosomes associated with it is not known for most cells, because the fixative most commonly used in electron-microscope studies of plant cells—potassium permanganate ($KMnO_4$)—does not preserve the ribosomes, although it preserves well other parts of the plant cell. In examining photographs of preparations made from tissue fixed in this way, it is important to remember that the ribosomes have been removed.

The composition of the ER and the ribosomes differ quite markedly from one another. The ER has the same general composition as the other membranes of the cell and consists primarily of lipids and proteins. In contrast, the ribosomes consist primarily of ribonucleic acid or RNA and protein.

The ER and the ribosomes appear to function as the sites of synthesis of several important cell constituents, including the fatty acids and the proteins. Fats and lipids are molecules composed of two basic parts: a special alcohol, usually one called glycerol, and fatty

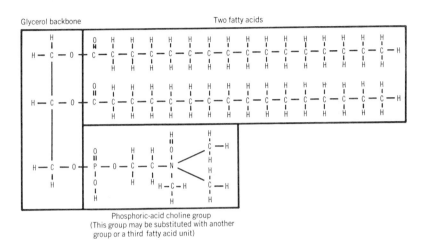

Phosphoric-acid choline group
(This group may be substituted with another
group or a third fatty acid unit)

Fig. 6-5. *Diagram of a lipid molecule (the phospholipid lecithin).*

acids (Fig. 6-5). Glycerol forms the backbone of the fat molecule. To the glycerol are attached either three fatty acids or two fatty acids and a third compound. The fatty acids are straight chain molecules, usually composed of from 16 to 18 carbon atoms, to which are attached oxygen and hydrogen atoms. Current evidence suggests that the fatty acids are made in the cytoplasm in association with the ER but that the lipid molecules themselves are synthesized in the mitochondria. The assembling of a lipid molecule begins with a reaction in which the fatty acid molecules are combined with a compound called coenzyme A (step A in Fig. 6-6). Three fatty-acid–coenzyme-A combinations next react with a glycerol molecule (step B). This results in the formation of a lipid molecule and the release of three coenzyme A molecules (step C). When formed, the lipids may be used in a variety of cell structures or they may be stored in special colorless

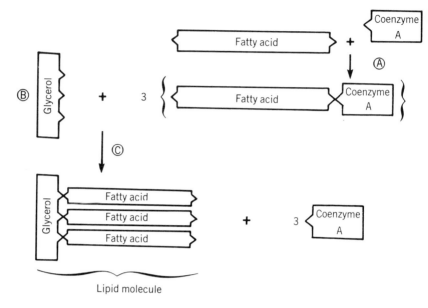

Fig. 6-6. *Outline of lipid formation.*

plastids, which are frequently found in seeds and the storage tissues of many plants.

THE RIBOSOMES AND PROTEIN SYNTHESIS

Proteins are complex molecules composed of long chains of amino acids. They are found in all parts of the cell. In addition, all enzymes are proteins. Because of their importance to the cell, the questions of how proteins are made and how their synthesis is controlled have been major issues for cytologists and biochemists. In recent years, the outlines of the answers to these questions have been discovered and many (but hardly all) of the details have been filled in.

The question of protein synthesis involves several points. First, there are some 20 amino acids involved; where are they formed? Second, each protein molecule contains hundreds of amino acids arranged in a precise order; how is this order determined and how is it achieved? Third, the number and type of proteins, particularly enzymes, is vitally connected with cell growth and function; what determines which proteins shall be made by the cell?

The site of amino-acid synthesis appears to be the mitochondria. As

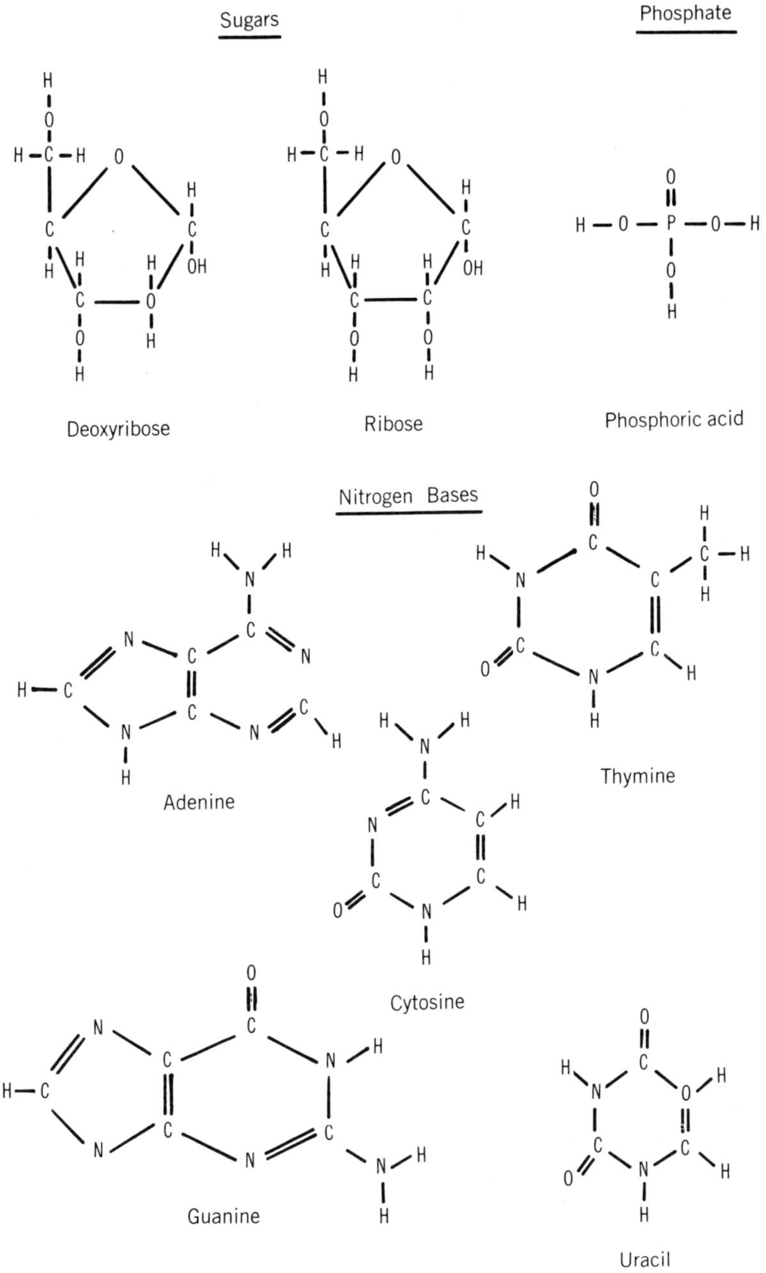

Fig. 6-7. *Chemical formula for the parts of RNA and DNA.*

indicated in Chapter 3, recent evidence indicates that the chloroplasts also produce amino acids. But neither the mitochondria nor the chloroplasts appear to be the major site of protein synthesis in the cell. The chloroplasts probably synthesize protein during development, but the bulk of protein synthesis takes place in the cytoplasm. The specific sites of protein synthesis are the ribosomes. It is at the ribosomes that the amino acids become connected to form protein molecules.

The ribosomes contain a highly significant chemical constituent—RNA (ribonucleic acid). There are two nucleic acids: RNA, which is found in the cytoplasm and the nucleus, and DNA (deoxyribonucleic acid), which is found primarily in the nucleus. The two nucleic acids are quite similar in composition and structure. Both are large molecules made of repeating units consisting of a sugar, a phosphate, and a nitrogen base (Fig. 6-7). There are two sugars involved. One, deoxyribose, is found only in DNA, while the second, ribose, is found only in RNA. A total of five nitrogen bases are present. Three bases are present in both RNA and DNA: adenine, guanine, and cytosine. In addition, DNA contains thymine and RNA contains uracil. The way these molecules are arranged to form either DNA or RNA is shown in Fig. 6-8.

Several types of RNA appear to be involved in protein synthesis. The first step in protein synthesis is the activation of the amino acids, which occurs through the union of an amino acid with an ATP molecule. The activated amino acid then combines with an RNA molecule with the release of an ADP molecule. This RNA is called *transfer RNA* and appears to be a relatively small, readily soluble molecule. The transfer RNA is amino acid specific, so that for each amino acid there is a special type of transfer RNA. After the transfer RNA combines with the amino acids, the amino acids are joined together, transfer RNA separates from the amino acids, and a protein molecule results. But the process of protein synthesis involves more than merely joining a group of amino acids together in a random arrangement. Each protein molecule is composed of amino acids arranged in a precise order. The order is determined at the ribosome in conjunction with messenger RNA. Recent work indicates that a strand of messenger RNA is actually associated with a cluster of ribosomes (Fig. 6-9). These clusters of ribosomes are called *polysomes* and may, with the attached messenger RNA, be the actual functional unit in protein synthesis.

The term *messenger RNA* is derived from the concept that the

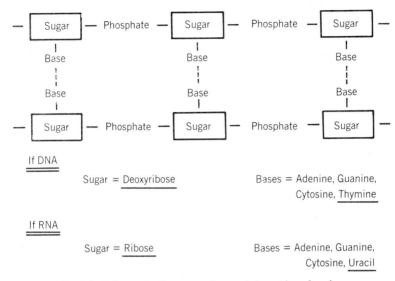

If DNA

Sugar = Deoxyribose   Bases = Adenine, Guanine,
                                     Cytosine, Thymine

If RNA

Sugar = Ribose   Bases = Adenine, Guanine,
                                     Cytosine, Uracil

Fig. 6-8. *Schematic diagram of a nucleic-acid molecule.*

genetic material of the cell that determines the heredity of the organism is located in the nucleus. There is a great deal of data to indicate that the genetic material is DNA and that the genes operate by influencing the synthesis of enzyme molecules. The principal site of DNA is the nucleus, while protein synthesis occurs in the cytoplasm. Hence a messenger is needed to convey the genetic information to the

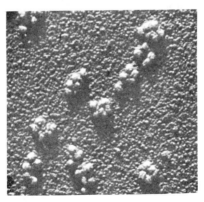

Fig. 6-9. *Polysomes from liver. Courtesy of Dr. J. R. Warner, Massachusetts Institute of Technology.*

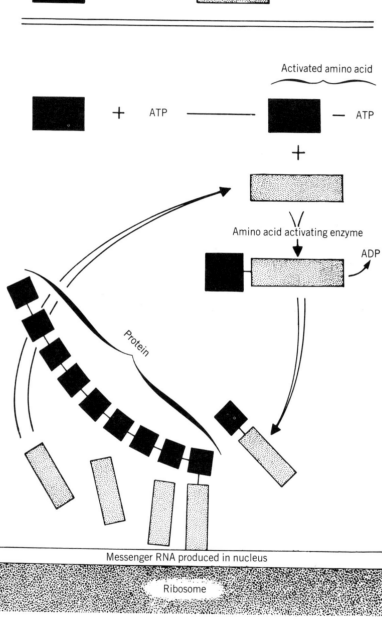

Fig. 6-10. *Diagram of protein synthesis indicating the possible roles of transfer RNA, messenger RNA, and the ribosome.*

cytoplasmic site of protein formation. This messenger appears to be a special type of RNA—consequently, the name "messenger RNA."

Messenger RNA is produced in the nucleus and moves to the cytoplasm, where, in conjunction with the ribosomes that contain additional RNA, it determines the sequence of amino acids present in the protein molecule. This occurrence is indicated diagrammatically in Fig. 6-10.

The way information is stored, reproduced, and transmitted in the nucleus is discussed in Chapters 7, 8, and 9. The basic pattern, however, is that the genetic information is embodied in the DNA molecule, transmitted through the RNA molecule, and used in the production of protein molecules.

7

THE NUCLEUS

THE CONTROL CENTER OF THE CELL

The nucleus (Fig. 7-1) is a universal and prominent feature of all cells except bacteria and blue-green algae. A few cells, such as the sieve-tube elements of plants and the red blood cells of animals, may lose their nuclei when they become mature, but all cells have nuclei at some time in their lives. Situated in the cytoplasm, it may occupy a major proportion of the cell volume in young, rapidly dividing cells (Fig. 6-1). In older cells it comprises a smaller part of the total volume of the cell and may become pressed between the vacuole and the wall (Fig. 7-2). Although most cells of the vascular plant have but a single nucleus, some cells have two or more. The latex tubes are one example of a multinucleate cell in a vascular plant. In many non-vascular plants, the cells have more than one nucleus. There are numerous cases in which there are large numbers of free nuclei in a mass of cytoplasm, as in the slime molds, or where the number of nuclei are more limited, as in many algae.

The major function of the nucleus is to control and direct the development of the cell. This control can be demonstrated in many ways, but one of the most dramatic is by experimentation using a relatively large green alga named *Acetabularia*. This alga grows in the form of a stalk with a characteristic expansion or cap at the top. Each alga is a single cell, with a nucleus situated in the basal part of the stalk. If the cap or top is cut off, the stalk will regenerate a new cap. The following experiment can be performed using two species of *Acetabularia,* each having a differently shaped top. The top of one species is removed. Next, the base containing the nucleus is cut off and a base, complete with nucleus, of the second species is grafted to the cut stalk. The stalk will regenerate a new top but this will not be of the original type; it will be the type characteristic of the species whose grafted base contained the nucleus. Thus, the information necessary for the formation of a regenerated top is present in the nucleus.

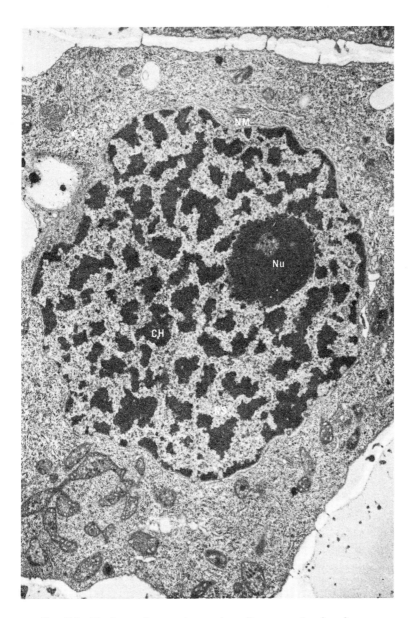

Fig. 7-1. *Nucleus of a meristematic cell as seen in the electron microscope. Ch: chromatin; NS: nuclear sap; Nu: nucleolus; NM: nuclear membrane. Compare this photograph with Fig. 1-2. These are two similar cells; Fig. 1-2 was prepared to show membrane distribution, Fig. 7-1 to retain nucleic acids that are lost in the first method.*

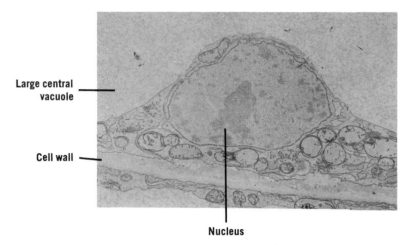

Large central vacuole

Cell wall

Nucleus

Fig. 7-2. *Nucleus of a highly vacuolate cell.*

The nucleus is the major site of the genetic material, and through the production of messenger RNA the information present in the nucleus is relayed to the cytoplasm. The nucleus is the control center of the cell. Within the nucleus is the genetic information, and through the action of the nucleus this information is translated into protein production in the cytoplasm.

Because of the importance and size of the nucleus, it has been studied intensively by cytologists for over a hundred years. The details of nuclear structure and nuclear reproduction were discovered in the last half of the 1800s; the presence of the hereditary material in the nucleus was found early in the 1900s; the role of the nucleus in regulating and directing protein production in the cytoplasm through RNA is a product of the last twenty years; and some knowledge of the ultrastructure of the nucleus is a development of the past ten years.

THE PARTS OF THE NUCLEUS

The nucleus is surrounded by a double membrane (Fig. 7-3). This membrane is characterized by extensions into the cytoplasm, which appear continuous with the ER, and by the presence of pores. The pores are easily visible in the electron microscope (see arrow, Fig. 7-3) and appear to be numerous. The question of whether the pores are

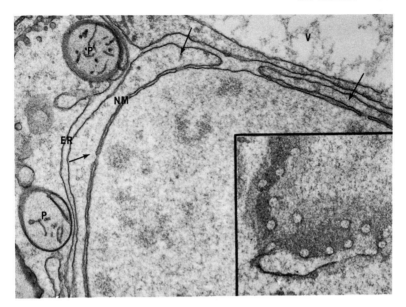

Fig. 7-3. *Nuclear membrane as seen in the electron microscope. Note pores in membrane (arrows). Insert shows face view of pores. NM: nuclear membrane; ER: endoplasmic reticulum; V: vacuole; P: plastid.*

actually open or not remains unsettled. In many preparations they appear open, as in Fig. 7-3, yet in some cases the same type of pore may, by different methods of preparation, show internal structures that may be plugs. Apparently in some cases the pores are essentially closed, while in others—the nuclei of yeast and onion roots, for example—they are open. The more universal pattern is unknown, as is the significance of their being open or closed.

The nuclear material in some cells—bacteria and blue-green algae, for example—is not limited by a membrane. In both examples a chromatin type of material is clearly present and usually more or less centrally located in the cell. There is no membrane surrounding this material and thus limiting it from the cytoplasm. This condition is considered more primitive than the case where a nuclear membrane is present. The significance of this lack of a limiting nuclear membrane is still not clear.

Within the nucleus, one or more bodies—the nucleoli (nucleolus, singular)—are visible (Fig. 7-1). These are roughly spherical in shape and may appear homogeneous or divided into two phases, one more dense than the other. In some cases the dense portion of the nucleolus can be resolved into a mass of closely packed dense spheres. The nucleoli are composed primarily of protein and RNA, although lipids and small amounts of DNA may be present.

The nucleus is filled with liquid called the *nuclear sap*. Within the nuclear sap, besides the nucleoli, are the nuclear ribosomes and the chromatin. The nuclear ribosomes are similar in size, shape, and composition to their cytoplasmic counterparts. The pores in the nuclear membrane are usually large enough to permit the passage of ribosomes, but whether or not such passage occurs is unknown. Movement of RNA from the nucleus to the cytoplasm is known and, as discussed in the previous chapter, is of great importance.

The chromatin of the nucleus is the genetic material. In the nondividing nucleus, the chromatin may not be distinct or may appear as a network of densely staining material. When the nucleus is about to reproduce through division, the chromatin becomes visible as darkly staining bodies—the chromosomes. Chemically the chromatin is composed of DNA and protein.

The DNA molecule consists of deoxyribose (a sugar), phosphates, and the nitrogen bases: adenine, thymine, guanine, and cytosine. The general structure of DNA is similar to RNA in that the molecule consists of a backbone of the sugars and phosphate, with the bases attached to this backbone through the sugar molecules. Two molecules of DNA are always found together and form a complimentary pair. The sugar-phosphate part of the molecule can be visualized as the side rails of a ladder with the bases paired to form the rungs. Actually, the DNA molecule is not straight, as is a ladder, but is twisted into the form of a helix (Fig. 7-4). The arrangement of the nitrogen bases follows a fixed pattern. This pattern is such that if an adenine forms one half of the rung of the ladder, thymine always forms the other half. In a similar manner, if guanine forms one half, cytosine always forms the other half. The order of adenine, thymine, guanine, and cytosine vertically in one half of the ladder may be in any pattern. What is always fixed, however, is the pairing of the bases in the manner indicated in Fig. 7-6—namely, adenine-thymine and guanine-cytosine.

This type of arrangement makes it easy to see how DNA can reproduce exactly. All that is necessary is for the two strands of DNA to separate (Fig. 7-5). Then, from a supply of units consisting of the nitrogen bases, plus deoxyribose and phosphate, an adenine unit would

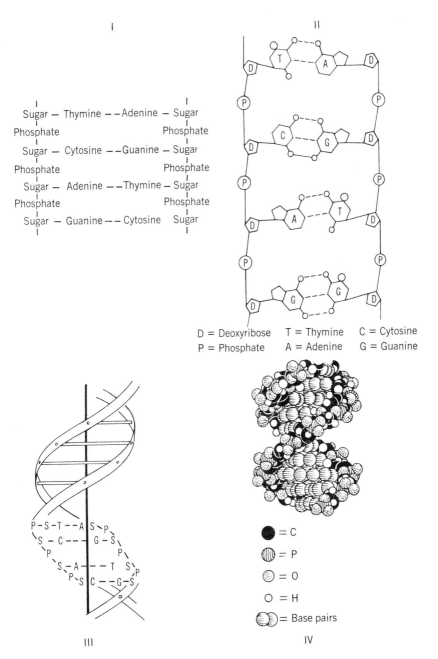

I

Sugar — Thymine — —Adenine — Sugar
Phosphate   Phosphate
Sugar — Cytosine — —Guanine — Sugar
Phosphate   Phosphate
Sugar — Adenine — —Thymine — Sugar
Phosphate   Phosphate
Sugar — Guanine — — Cytosine Sugar

II

D = Deoxyribose T = Thymine C = Cytosine
P = Phosphate   A = Adenine G = Guanine

P-S-T--A S-P
S - C --- G-S P
P S-A--- T S P
P-S C — -G-S

● = C
◐ = P
◉ = O
○ = H
◐◑ = Base pairs

III   IV

Fig. 7-4. *Diagram of DNA (Watson-Crick model).*

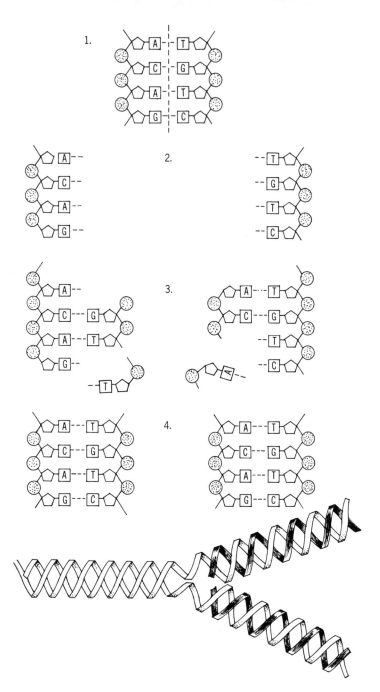

Fig. 7-5. *Diagrammatic representation of the postulated method of DNA duplication. By permission of* Scientific American.

pair with the thymine of one strand, and a thymine unit would pair with the adenine in the second strand. This type of pairing would occur for all the bases, as shown in Fig. 7-5. Then a backbone would form, by the union of the individual base units, making two complete DNA molecules. Each is identical to the original and each is composed of half the original. Considerable evidence exists indicating that this type of reproduction of DNA actually occurs within the cell. The importance of the structure of the DNA molecule to the storing of genetic information will be discussed more fully in Chapter 9.

The proteins found in the nucleus, particularly in conjunction with the nucleoli and the chromatin, are also unique. They contain high amounts of certain of the amino acids and are termed *basic* proteins. The basic protein most commonly found in nuclei is named *histone*. The role of histone in the functioning of the nucleus is not yet known, but existing data indicate that histone may play an important role in the functioning of DNA.

THE NUCLEUS AND DNA

The amount of DNA in the nucleus of the cell and the time of formation of DNA has been widely studied by cytologists. The interest in this type of information stems from the consideration of DNA as the genetical material. Two requirements of any substance that may be the genetical material of the cell are that it be constant in amount during the nondividing phase of the life of the cell and that it precisely double sometime before the division of the nucleus. These requirements are met by DNA.

Two techniques have been widely used in the study of DNA in the cell. One is microspectrophotometry, and the other is autoradiography. Both of these procedures have applications beyond the study of DNA—particularly autoradiography—but both have been so widely applied to the DNA question that they will be described here.

In microspectrophotometry the aim is to measure the amount of a substance, such as DNA, by determining the amount of color produced when the substance is caused to react with a dye. A colored object, as noted in Chapter 3, absorbs light. Thus, if there is a way to measure the amount of light absorbed, the amount of the substance can be measured. In the case of a microspectrophotometer, light of a known color (i.e., wave length) is passed through a microscope (Fig. 7-6). The eyepiece of the microscope contains a sensitive photocell attached to an electrical measuring device. One measurement is taken in a

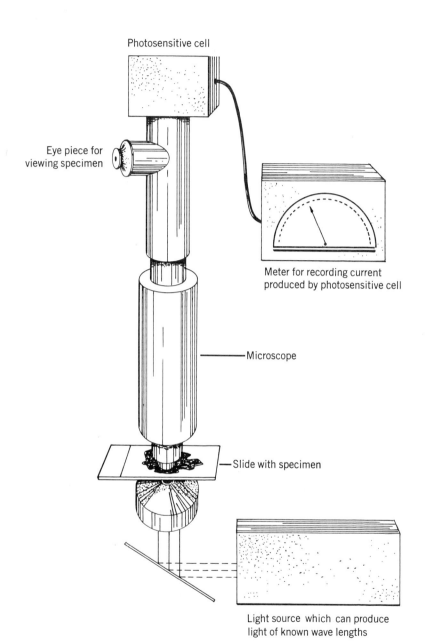

Photosensitive cell

Eye piece for
viewing specimen

Meter for recording current
produced by photosensitive cell

Microscope

Slide with specimen

Light source which can produce
light of known wave lengths

Fig. 7-6. *Drawing of a microspectrophotometer.*

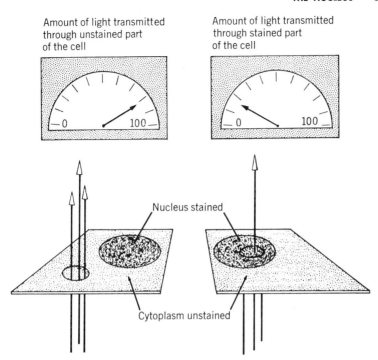

Amount of light transmitted through unstained part of the cell

Amount of light transmitted through stained part of the cell

Nucleus stained

Cytoplasm unstained

Fig. 7-7. *Diagram of the method of making a measurement in a microspectrophotometer.*

clear part of the cell and a second is taken in the colored part (Fig. 7-7). The difference in these two measurements represents the amount of light absorbed and, indirectly, the amount of the substance.

Fundamental to microspectrophotometry is the requirement that the amount of color produced be directly proportional to the amount of the substance present. Such proportional reactions are rare, and it is one of the fortunate accidents of science that this type of reaction—called the Feulgen reaction—was found for DNA. Studies based on the measurement of the color produced by the Feulgen reaction have contributed significantly to the concept that DNA is the genetic material.

Autoradiography is based on completely different principles. In this procedure, advantage is taken of the fact that the radiations emitted by radioactive compounds will expose photographic film in a manner similar to light. The first step in the procedure is the placing of the cell in a solution of a compound containing radioactive atoms (Fig. 7-8). For example, thymine containing radioactive carbon atoms may be

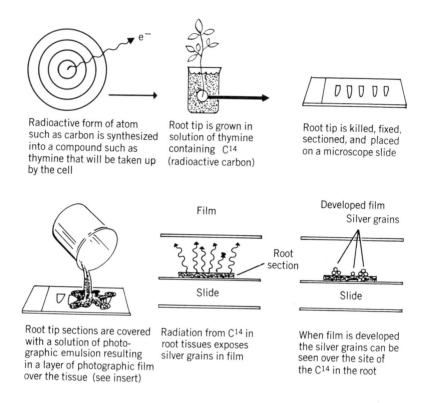

Radioactive form of atom such as carbon is synthesized into a compound such as thymine that will be taken up by the cell

Root tip is grown in solution of thymine containing C^{14} (radioactive carbon)

Root tip is killed, fixed, sectioned, and placed on a microscope slide

Root tip sections are covered with a solution of photographic emulsion resulting in a layer of photographic film over the tissue (see insert)

Radiation from C^{14} in root tissues exposes silver grains in film

When film is developed the silver grains can be seen over the site of the C^{14} in the root

Fig. 7-8. *Outline of the procedure of autoradiography.*

used. When the cell has incorporated this compound into its own chemical structure (DNA in the case of thymine), the cell is placed on a microscope slide and covered with an extremely thin layer of photographic film. This process is done in the dark, and the tissue and film are kept in the dark for a number of days. The film is then developed by the usual photographic methods. The final preparation is viewed under the microscope. What is seen is a deposit of silver grains over the site of the radioactive compound (Fig. 7-9). The black areas in a regular photographic negative are composed of dense concentrations of silver grains produced as a result of the action of light and the developing of the original film. The same is true for an autoradiograph except that the radiation is not from light but from radioactivity and, instead of appearing as a dark mass of silver grains, the grains are seen individually. In the case of radioactive thymine,

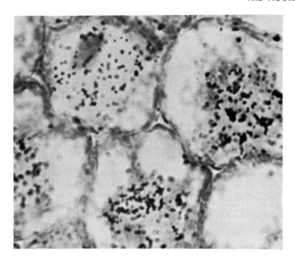

Fig. 7-9. *Autoradiograph of a nucleus that incorporated a nucleic-acid precursor.*

most of the silver grains would be limited in distribution to the nuclear area.

The actual method of autoradiography is more complicated than indicated here. The major advantage of autoradiography is the versatility and sensitivity of the method. All types of problems and tissues have been studied by this method.

The data from autoradiographic and microspectrophotometric studies from a wide range of cells substantiates the concept of DNA constancy. In the root, for example, where there are many cells in division, it can be shown that the amount of DNA remains at a given level during most of the life of the cell. Prior to the division of the nucleus, the amount of DNA doubles. During division this amount is precisely halved. This data fits well with the concept of DNA as the genetic material and with the facts of nuclear division discussed in Chapter 8.

There is another phenomenon involving DNA which occurs in many plant cells. In the root, above the area of cell division, DNA content continues to increase, but, as nuclear divisions diminish, the DNA amount is not reduced. Thus, there is an increase in DNA per nucleus. The amount is always in precise, even multiples of the original base amount found in the nucleus. This phenomenon is found in all parts of the plant and it is believed that the vast majority of plant cells contain more than the base amount of DNA.

The meaning of this observation is not clear. The fact that those cells of the vascular plant that normally divide and give rise to new organs, such as secondary roots, have only the base amount of DNA while the cells that normally do not divide again have multiples of this amount indicates that in some manner the amount of DNA present may influence the potential development of the cell.

THE PHYSIOLOGICAL ROLE
OF THE NUCLEUS

The cell functions as an integrated whole with each part involved in a specific set of reactions that contribute to the maintenance and growth of the cell. Yet each part reacts with others and all are interdependent.

The chloroplasts convert light energy into chemical energy in the form of carbohydrates. This energy is transferred to ATP molecules in the mitochondria. Some of this energy is used to activate amino acids produced in the mitochondria and chloroplasts so that the amino acids can be synthesized into protein by the ribosomes. Other ATPs are used in the synthesis of fatty acids by the ER and the assembly of these into lipids by the mitochondria. The nucleus supplies RNA to the cytoplasm, which provides the pattern for the assembly of the amino acids into protein. These patterns in turn reflect the genetic material of the cell present in the nucleus in the form of the DNA molecule. The nucleus, in turn, is dependent on the mitochondria for the energy-requiring processes taking place within it. Energy, protein, and lipid synthesis are all necessary if the cell and vacuole membranes are to exist; and without these membranes the cell cannot exist.

The nucleus plays an important role in the cell—not because it is directly involved in energy transformation, as is the case for the chloroplasts and the mitochondria, but because it supplies the key to the entire long-range functioning of the cell through the direction and control of protein synthesis. Virtually every reaction in the cell is controlled by enzymes, and all enzymes are proteins. A cell deprived of its nucleus does not die immediately, and if it contains chloroplasts it may live for reasonably long periods of time; but in all cases the functioning of the cell is altered. In the intact living cell, if any one part can be considered to be the control center, that part is the nucleus.

The cell is in almost constant need to produce both protein and RNA, because many proteins appear to have a definite life span after which they are broken down and replaced by new protein molecules. Consequently, in almost all cells protein synthesis is a normal function of the cell so long as it is alive. The life span of some types of RNA, particularly messenger RNA, is short and, because of the essential role these RNA molecules play in protein synthesis, they are constantly being synthesized by the nucleus.

At all times, whether during growth or at rest, the cell requires the synthesis of materials under the control of the nucleus. It is during growth, however, that the nucleus becomes the dominant, directive force in the cell. The genes that are present in the nucleus determine the direction of development of the cell.

8

MITOSIS

CELL REPRODUCTION

For an organism to grow and survive, the cells of which it is composed must be capable of reproduction. In the vast majority of organisms, cell reproduction or *mitosis* involves two synchronized processes. The first of these processes—*karyokinesis* or nuclear division—is the division of the nucleus into two. The second process—*cytokinesis* or cytoplasmic division—involves the division of the cell so that each half receives one nucleus. In most cases, nuclear and cytoplasmic division are closely connected in time. There are cases, however, in which the nuclei undergo repeated divisions without the occurrence of cytoplasmic division. In the multinucleate cells that result, cell divisions may occur at a later time and are not connected with mitosis.

Nuclear and cytoplasmic division are two of the most complex processes in the biological world. Although the cell can hardly be considered static in the nondividing state, during division it passes through a dramatic continuum of change and movement. So large a number of changes occur at the same time or overlap to such an extent that description becomes difficult.

During the process of mitosis, the nucleus divides. A series of changes occurs in the form and content of the nucleus, with the result that two daughter nuclei are produced from the original nucleus (Fig. 8-1). The entire process is one of constant, integrated change, with one event flowing into the next.

The first indication of mitosis is a change in the appearance of the nucleus. The nucleus becomes filled with condensing coils of darkly staining material. These coils continue to condense until they can be resolved into individual units or chromosomes. While this condensation of the chromosomes is occurring, the area around the nucleus

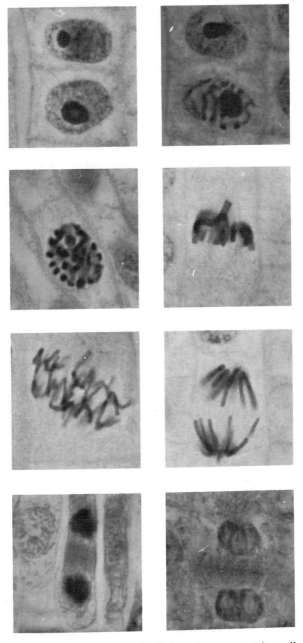

Fig. 8-1. *Mitosis as seen in the light microscope. The cells are from onion root tips.*

becomes free of the larger cell parts, such as mitochondria and plastids. The area thus formed is called the *clear zone.*

At this point the nuclear membrane dissolves and the nucleoli disappear. The chromosomes move to a central position in the region formerly delimited by the nuclear membrane. On each chromosome a specialized area, the *centromere,* is apparent. Fibers become attached to the centromere. These fibers extend from the centromeres to the opposite ends of the region occupied by the nucleus, called the *poles.* Fibers also extend directly from pole to pole. This apparatus, composed of a mass of fibers, is termed the *spindle,* and the fibers are called *spindle fibers.*

Each chromosome can be seen to be composed of two identical halves joined only at the centromere. After the centromeres of all the chromosomes are arranged in a horizontal or equatorial plate halfway between the poles, the centromeres divide and one half of each chromosome moves to the opposite pole. When the new chromosomes reach the poles, they form a group and a new nuclear membrane appears. The early stages of mitosis are now reversed and two complete new nuclei result.

While the chromosomes are moving to the poles, the fibers that extend from pole to pole become more dense in appearance in the center, equidistant from the poles. Small round bodies, apparently produced by the Golgi bodies, appear and gather in this area and result in the formation of the *cell plate.* The cell plate, which is the first stage in the formation of a new wall, forms initially in the region of the spindle and then spreads outward toward the margin of the cell. Finally the cell plate makes contact with the mature cell wall of the original cell, completing the process of division. Further changes occur in the cell plate and it is incorporated into the new cell wall.

This outline of mitosis is designed to indicate the major aspects of the process and to convey a sense of continuity of the action involved. For a more detailed description of mitosis, consider it as occurring in a number of steps (Fig. 8-2)—*prophase, metaphase, anaphase,* and *telophase.* Prophase covers the early changes in the nucleus and continues to the point at which the nuclear membrane disappears. Metaphase includes the placement of the centromeres on the equatorial plate and ends with the division of the centromeres and the movement of the chromosomes to the poles. The actual movement of the chromosomes occurs during anaphase. Telophase begins as the chromosomes reach the poles and the nuclear membrane reforms, and it continues until the interphase nuclear condition is re-established. In addition, the changes that occur before the nucleus divides must be considered and can be termed the *preparation* for division.

The division of a continuous process, such as mitosis, into parts is arbitrary. That mitosis can be discussed in a series of steps is less important, therefore, than that it is a single continuous process resulting in the reproduction of the nucleus.

Preparation for Mitosis

For mitosis to occur, a number of preliminary steps must take place in the nucleus and the cytoplasm. A variety of experimental evidence indicates that the control of division is largely a function of the cytoplasm. This control may take a number of forms, including the involvement of specific growth-regulating substances. Another factor is the supply of energy.

Energy is necessary for mitosis. The nucleus is not the site of reactions that yield large amounts of energy. Furthermore, during mitosis itself there is evidence indicating that respiration is low. Consequently, before mitosis can occur, sufficiently large supplies of readily available energy must be accumulated so that the process can be carried through to completion. If such energy is not available, mitosis will not begin. Once mitosis has begun, however, it continues to completion and is almost entirely independent of environmental changes that affect the energy supply.

The duplication of the chromosomes is another important part of the preparation for mitosis. Mitosis itself is not the process of chromosome reduplication. It is the mechanism by which the separation of duplicated chromosomes is achieved and the full complement of chromosomes is distributed to the two new nuclei. The actual duplication of the chromosomes occurs before prophase.

The synthesis of DNA takes place sometime before mitosis starts. Procedures described in Chapter 7 permit the measurement of the DNA content in individual nuclei. Numerous measurements of this type in plant and animal cells show that the DNA of the nucleus exactly doubles before prophase begins. A graph of the changes in DNA content of a nucleus during mitosis is shown in Fig. 8-3.

The proteins associated with the chromosomes, the *histones*, are also synthesized before prophase begins. The chemical components of the chromosomes all appear to be synthesized before mitosis occurs.

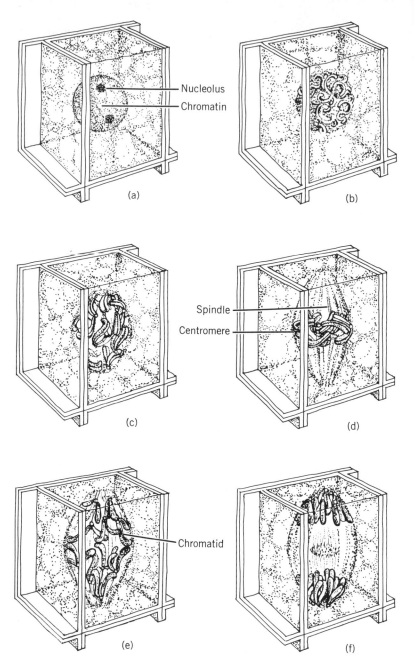

Fig. 8-2. *Diagram of mitosis. From Greulach and Adams,* Plants: An Introduction to Modern Botany (*John Wiley & Sons, Inc., 1962*), *by permission.*

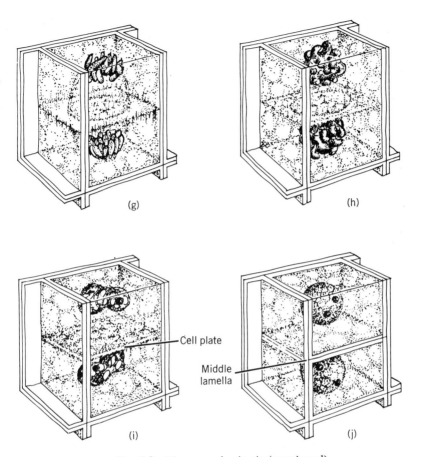

(g)

(h)

Cell plate

Middle
lamella

(i)

(j)

Fig. 8-2. *Diagram of mitosis (continued).*

Prophase

The beginning of mitosis is marked by the condensation of the chromosomes. In the nucleus of the nondividing cell, the chromosomes are expanded to their maximum length. They may become so diffuse in appearance that they cannot be seen. With the beginning of prophase, chromosomes progressively shorten and thicken through a coiling mechanism. As the chromosomes shorten, their form becomes increasingly clear. A chromosome consists of two segments, called *chromatids* (see Fig. 8-1). These are independent except in one region, the centromere. The region of the centromere is usually visible as a lighter-staining constriction in the chromosome.

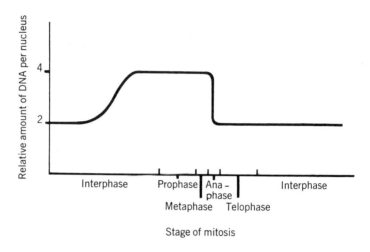

Fig. 8-3. *Changes in the DNA content of a nucleus during mitosis.*

While the chromosomes are condensing in the nucleus, a clear area is formed around the nucleus. In this zone the mitochondria, plastids, and similar large cell parts are excluded. This clear zone is ellipsoidal in shape, while the nucleus is spherical. The position of the poles and, hence, the plane of division are indicated by the location of the poles of the ellipse. The clear zone is apparently composed of the protein and other materials that will compose the bulk of the spindle when it is formed.

Prophase ends with the breakdown of the nuclear membrane and the dissolution of the nucleoli. The removal of the nuclear membrane results in the interspersion of the material of the clear zone with the nuclear substance.

Metaphase

As the nuclear membrane breaks down, the chromosomes begin a rather intricate pattern of movements, which result in the alignment of the centromeres on a plane perpendicular to the axis of the spindle and midway between the poles. This is the metaphase or *equatorial plate*. If the chromosomes are large, only the centromeres are arranged on the plate; if the chromosomes are small, the entire chromosome complement may be arranged on the plate.

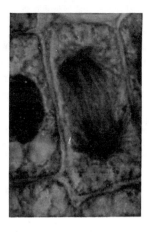

Fig. 8-4. *Spindle fibers as seen in the light microscope. The cell is from an onion root tip.*

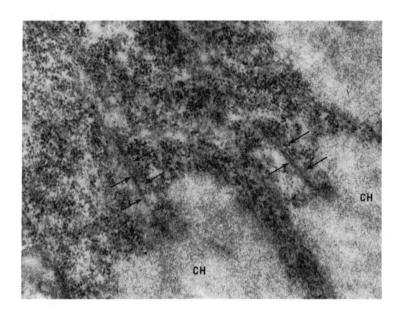

Fig. 8-5. *Spindle fibers as seen in the electron microscope. The cell is from a pea root tip. CH: chromosomes. Arrows indicate spindle fibers; round bodies are ribosomes. Courtesy of Dr. Patricia Harris, U. of California, Berkeley.*

The spindle now becomes clearly visible (Fig. 8-4). Some of its fibers extend from the centromeres of the chromosomes to the poles and are termed *chromosomal spindle fibers*. Other fibers that reach from pole to pole and are not attached to the chromosomes are called the *continuous spindle fibers*. In the electron microscope, the fibers appear tubular (Fig. 8-5).

The composition of the spindle is known primarily from analyses of isolated spindles from sea urchin and starfish eggs. These data and some supplementary evidence indicate that the spindle is composed mainly of protein and a small amount of RNA. Lipids are also known to be part of the spindle. The protein involved appears to be a product of the cytoplasm rather than the nucleus.

Anaphase

After all the centromeres are aligned on the plate, the centromere region of each chromosome separates and the two chromatids become independent of one another. At this point each chromatid becomes a chromosome. The chromosomes now begin moving toward the poles; one of each pair of new chromosomes moves to the opposite pole.

The movement of a chromosome depends on the presence of the spindle and the centromere. If the spindle is disrupted, as it is when the cell is treated with various drugs, no chromosome movement occurs. If the chromosome lacks a centromere, it will not migrate to the pole and will be lost to the nucleus. While the chromosomes are moving toward the poles, the poles move away from each other.

The mechanism of chromosome movement and the movement of the poles are not yet understood. The chromosomal spindle fibers appear to shorten and the continuous spindle fibers to lengthen, but the means by which these changes are accomplished is not known. Presumably ATP is involved as the energy source. The shortening of the chromosomal fibers does not appear to be a purely physical phenomenon such as the contraction of a stretched rubber band, nor does it appear to be a simple modification of the mechanism used in muscle contraction. An understanding of the mechanism of chromosome movement is one of the outstanding challenges to current cytological research.

Telophase

When the chromosomes reach the poles, they form a compact group, and the nuclear membrane forms. The chromosomes reverse their coiling, becoming longer and more diffuse in appearance. The nucleoli reappear. These changes occur during the final stage of mitosis—telophase.

The nuclear membrane and the endoplasmic reticulum are apparently continuous in the nondividing cell. During late anaphase and telophase the nuclear membrane appears to be reformed from the endoplasmic reticulum. Thus, the continuity between the nuclear membrane and the ER of the cytoplasm, which existed before division, is re-established. However, the details of the formation of the nuclear membrane are still not known.

In anaphase and early telophase, with organisms favorable for cytological observation, each new chromosome can be seen to consist of two chromatids. During the period beginning with the end of one telophase and ending with the beginning of the following prophase, these chromatids are duplicated. The coiling and uncoiling of the chromosomes and the chromatids is an involved and complicated process for which the underlying mechanism is unknown.

Cytoplasmic Division or Cytokinesis

As the chromosomes approach the poles, the continuous spindle fibers change. In the region of the equatorial plate they become increasingly dense and more fibrillar in appearance. This region is now termed the *phragmoplast*. Small droplets or granular bodies, semi-liquid in consistency, appear and migrate to the phragmoplast, where they fuse to form the cell plate (Fig. 8-6). The droplets appear as small vesicles in the electron microscope and presumably contain pectic substances or similar cell-wall constituents. These vesicles may be a product of the Golgi bodies (Fig. 8-7).

Next, the phragmoplast extends toward the side walls of the cell. The fusion of additional droplets to the cell plate extends the plate until it reaches the existing walls. The cell plate probably forms the middle lamella on which the new primary walls are built. Present knowledge of this stage of cell division is also incomplete.

Duration of Mitosis

The lengths of time involved in the various stages of mitosis vary from organism to organism as well as under various environmental conditions. The various stages of mitosis are not all equal in duration and show marked variation.

Prophase is usually the longest stage, lasting one to two or more hours. The duration of metaphase is much shorter and is in the range

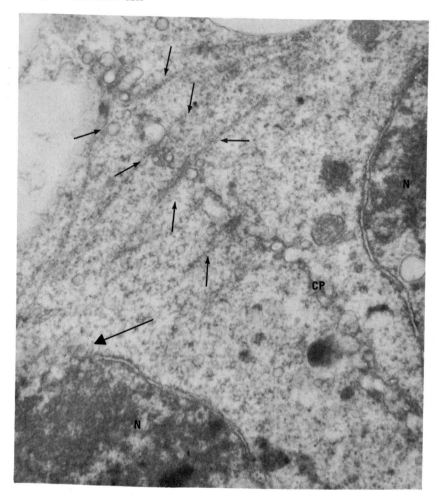

Fig. 8-6. *Formation of the cell plate as seen in the electron microscope. N: nucleus; CP: cell plate. Small arrows point to fibers of the phragmoplast; double arrow indicates a region of the nucleus where the nuclear membrane is not yet completely formed.*

of 5 to 15 minutes. Anaphase is usually the shortest stage and is only 2 to 10 minutes in length. Finally, telophase may vary from 10 to 30 minutes. These figures indicate the relative lengths of the various stages and should not be considered exact limits.

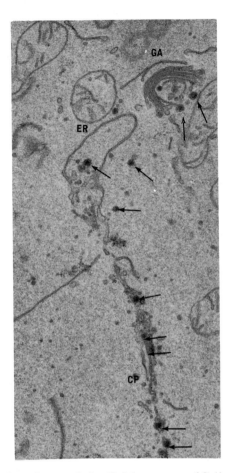

Fig. 8-7. *The relation of the Golgi apparatus (GA) to the formation of the cell plate. The arrows indicate vesicles produced by the Golgi apparatus and their incorporation into the cell plate (CP). ER: endoplasmic reticulum. Courtesy of Dr. H. Mollenhauer, U. of Texas.*

Variations in Mitosis

The pattern of mitosis just described is characteristic of most plant cells. Differences in detail exist, however, in some algae, fungi, and vascular plants, and in most animals, particularly with regard to the spindle.

Adjacent to the nuclear membrane but in the cytoplasm of many of these cells is a pair of dense bodies called *centrioles*. Centrioles are particularly characteristic of animal cells but are also found in some plant cells. Each centriole consists of a pair of small cylinders having walls composed of nine groups of three smaller tubules. The two small cylinders usually lie at right angles to each other. At the beginning of prophase, the two centrioles move apart and the spindle begins to form. The spindle is usually extensive, with spindle fibers radiating out into the cytoplasm. In some cases in plants, true centrioles are lacking, and the poles of the spindle consist of dense granular bodies. When the chromosomes reach the poles and the nuclear membrane begins to reappear, the centrioles reproduce so that each new nucleus has two centrioles.

Centrioles appear closely associated with motility of the reproductive cells. These motile cells have flagella, and usually associated with the base of the flagella is a centriole or a modification of the centriole. In plants such as the ferns and pines, where only the sperm have flagella, only the sperm cells have centrioles, which appear in the last divisions that produce the sperm.

Only the most general patterns of mitosis and cell division have been discussed in this chapter, and many variations occur. Indeed, almost every conceivable modification can and does occur in some organism. The major variations are outlined at the end of this chapter.

The dissociation of mitosis and cell division was noted earlier in this chapter. Many plants are composed of a single large cell possessing many nuclei that divide without subsequent wall formation. In some cells, several nuclear divisions may occur, followed by many simultaneous cell divisions.

There are many other variations involving all phases of mitosis. For example, although the nuclear membrane usually disappears at the end of prophase, in some organisms it may persist throughout the division. Similarly, although the spindle usually forms in the cytoplasm or after the nuclear membrane disappears, the spindle may actually form within the nuclear membrane. The cells of most vascular plants do not have centrioles, although a few do. The vast majority of chromosomes have a single distinct centromere, but a few plants and animals have chromosomes that lack clear centromeres; instead, their chromosomes have numerous points of spindle-fiber attachment.

Mitosis and cell division are such vital processes that, regardless of the many variations that have been recorded, the fundamental task of chromosome separation is always achieved.

MAJOR VARIATIONS OF THE SCHEME OF CELL DIVISION*

I. Mitosis leading to the formation of separate daughter nuclei.
  A. Nuclear behavior during prophase.
    1. Nuclear membrane disappears (most plants and animals).
    2. Nuclear membrane persists through division (many protozoa, some animals).
  B. Chromosome alignment at metaphase.
    1. All of chromosomes contained in "metaphase plate" (many large cells with small chromosomes).
    2. Centromeres only aligned on equatorial plane. Arms of chromosomes dangle from equatorial plane (many small cells with large chromosomes).
    3. Equatorial alignment not evident. Chromosomes may lie entirely outside continuous spindle, connected to poles by chromosomal fibers. "Metaphase plate" may lie obliquely to axis of spindle (pollen tubes).
  C. Spindle form.
    1. Continuous spindle fibers from pole to pole intermingled with chromosomal fibers connecting chromosomes to poles (many plant and animal cells).
    2. Continuous "central spindle" may be distinct from "half spindles" connecting chromosomes to poles. Chromosomes may be arrayed around circumference of central spindle (many plant and animal cells).
    3. Spindles function entirely within nuclear membrane (many protozoa; some plant and animal cells).
    4. Each chromosome may move within a distinct spindle element of its own (certain insects).
  D. Mitotic centers.
    1. Distinct centers with asters. Centers may be in the form of condensed centrioles observable by staining, centrioles laying in a larger "centrosome," or large "centrospheres" without distinct staining centrioles (most animals, many lower plants).
    2. No differentiated structure at the poles that may be identified by observation (most higher plants).
  E. Chromosome-to-pole connections and chromosome movement.
    1. Chromosomes move toward poles as chromosomal fibers shorten. Shape of chromosomes compatible with hypothesis that they are being dragged by attachment at a single point (most plant and animal cells).
    2. Chromosomes behave as though they are being dragged by fibers attached along their entire length (diffuse centromere) (some plant cells).

* Taken from "Materials for the Biophysical and Biochemical Study of Cell Division" by Daniel Mazia, in *Advances in Biological and Medical Physics,* Vol. 4 (Academic Press Inc., 1956), pp. 69–118. By permission.

      3. Chromosomes move "wrong way." Fibers seem to elongate and ends of arms move ahead of centromere (some insect cells).
F. Relative rates of movement of individual chromosomes.
      1. All chromosomes move at the same rate, independent of size (most cases).
      2. A certain chromosome moves at a different rate from all the rest.
G. Elongation of spindle and shortening of chromosomal fibers.
      1. Chromosome sets may separate by simultaneous shortening of chromosomal fibers and elongation of spindle.
      2. Shortening of the chromosomal fibers may precede elongation of spindle. There is insufficient evidence for generalization about which is the more common pattern.
H. Cytokinesis; segregation of daughter nuclei in separate cells.
      1. "Furrowing" at equator. May take place simultaneously around circumference or may begin toward one side (egg cells in animals).
      2. Furrowing displaced toward one pole. Often associated with asymmetry of asters; smaller aster toward pole where small cell will form (occasional animal cells).
      3. Furrowing accompanied by pulling away of daughter cells, sometimes with stalk between daughter cells (many types of animal cells, especially ameboid cells).
      4. Furrowing along irregular path that seems to be determined by surface differentiation of cell (some ciliate protozoa).
      5. Laying down of new cell membrane and cell wall between daughter cells without furrowing (most plant cells).
      6. Nuclear division without cytoplasmic division, leading to the formation of syncytia, multinucleated masses (muscle tissue of animals, some slime molds, etc.). Sometimes the syncytium later partitions itself into cells by laying down membranes between nuclei (plant endosperms, spore formation in protozoa, etc.).
II. Chromosome multiplication and growth without formation of daughter nuclei or new cells.
A. Endomitosis. Cycles of doubling number of chromosomes within nucleus without separation of daughter sets. Cytoplasm grows parallel to increase in ploidy (some plant cells and cells of some insect tissues).
B. Polyteny. Number of genetic strands per chromosome doubles in a cyclic fashion; chromosome number does not change; cytoplasm grows in proportion to number of times the chromosome strands have doubled ("giant cells" of fly larvae).

9

MEIOSIS,

CHROMOSOMES,

AND GENES

MEIOSIS

Mitosis is not the only type of division that can occur in plant and animal cells. A second type is found in specialized cells of both plants and animals. In this second type of nuclear division, termed *meiosis,* the chromosomes are not divided so that each daughter nucleus has the same number of chromosomes as the original cell, as in mitosis. Instead they are reduced in number so that each daughter nucleus receives precisely one-half of the original number of chromosomes.

Meiosis is associated with reproductive or sex cells. The egg and sperm in animals and some plants are produced directly through meiosis. At fertilization the egg and sperm nuclei fuse and the original chromosome number is re-established. In most plants, meiosis is not directly linked to the formation of sex cells. Instead, the nuclei and the cells that result from meiosis divide several or many times by mitosis before sex cells are differentiated. The green algae, for example, usually have the reduced, or haploid, chromosome number during the major part of their life cycles and the full, or diploid, chromosome number for only a short period. Thus, meiosis must be considered as a reduction division and not as the division that always results in the formation of sex cells.

The mechanics of meiosis are more involved than those of mitosis (Fig. 9-1). Two closely coordinated divisions constitute meiosis (Fig. 9-2). In the first division (meiosis I), the chromosome number is halved; in the second division (meiosis II), the reduced number is reproduced. This means that every meiotic division results in four

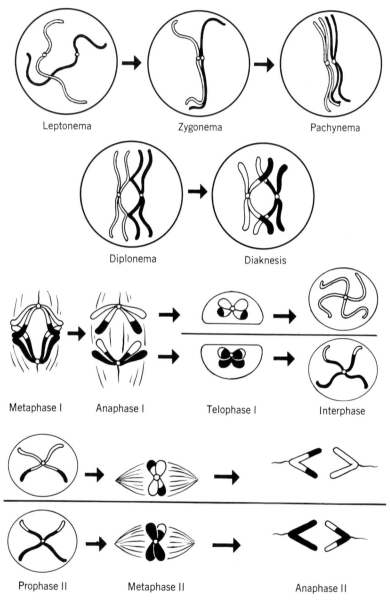

Fig. 9-1. *Stages of meiosis. The names are those applied to the various stages of division.*

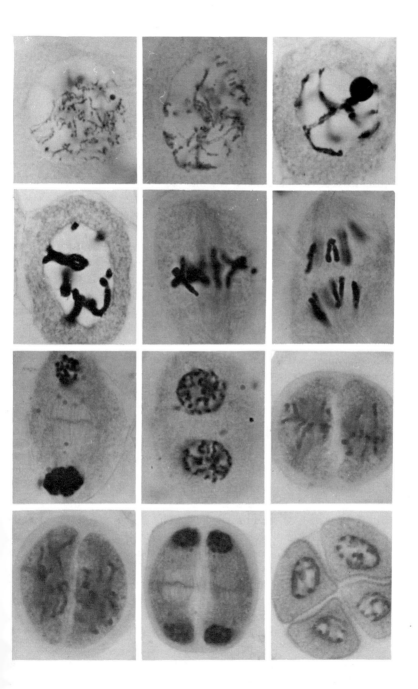

Fig. 9-2. *Meiosis as seen in the light microscope. (Lily anthers.)*

nuclei, each with one-half of the chromosome number present in the original nucleus.

The prophase of the first division of meiosis is long and elaborate. During the early stages, the chromosomes condense as they do in mitosis, except that the chromosomes appear longer and thinner and are composed of a single chromatid. Next, the chromosomes pair.

The chromosomes in a diploid cell are present in sets of two. Thus, the diploid-chromosome number is always an even number, and a chromosome complement of six may be composed of two long, two medium, and two short chromosomes. Except during meiosis, the *homologous chromosomes,* as the pairs are called, act independently of one another. During prophase of meiosis I, the homologous chromosomes become aligned. This alignment of the two chromosomes is precise, and they are exactly matched throughout their length. The shortening of the chromosomes continues, and each of the aligned chromosomes can now be resolved as two chromatids.

Next, the pair of chromosomes appear to repel one another. Instead of separating, however, they are held together at points where parts of their chromatids have been exchanged. These points are called *chiasmata.* At first the chromatids appear simply to lie across one another, but then it is believed that a break and recombination occurs and pieces of chromatids are actually exchanged between the chromosomes. When the exchange is completed, the chromosomes are essentially free of one another and are able to separate. This marks the end of the prophase of meiosis I.

At metaphase I, the centromeres of the chromosomes do not divide, and the chromatids of each chromosome are held together. During anaphase, as a result, the original chromosomes move toward the poles—one homologous chromosome migrating to one pole while the other moves to the opposite pole. This is the period of reduction in chromosome number, because each group of moving chromosomes is half the original number present in the nucleus. Telophase is essentially the same as in mitosis.

Meiosis II may begin almost as soon as meiosis I is complete. In some cases, however, the two divisions may be separated by a time interval of hours to months. The prophase that begins the second meiotic division is uncomplicated compared to that of prophase I and closely resembles the prophase of mitosis. At metaphase, the centromere divides and the chromatids finally separate to form two new chromosomes. These chromosomes are not identical, as in the case of mitosis, because of the exchange of segments of the chromatid between the homologous chromosomes during meiosis I. Anaphase and telophase are the same as in mitosis or meiosis I.

It is evident from even this brief discussion that meiosis is a highly complex phenomenon. Because of its unique features and importance, it has been extensively studied in many organisms. The names that have been assigned to the various parts of the process are indicated in Figs. 9-1 and 9-2. Both mitosis and meiosis are difficult problems for the cytologist to approach experimentally, yet they present challenges of great magnitude to the biologist.

MEIOSIS AND GENES

Meiosis is an elaborate mechanism for the separation of homologous chromosomes. These chromosomes are united again when the sex cells or gametes fuse. The question that immediately arises is, Why is such an elaborate procedure necessary to secure such a simple result? The answer is that the result is far from simple and that the separation and recombination of the chromosomes is highly significant to the organism. To understand this answer, it is necessary to examine more closely the nature of the chromosomes and to discuss the genes.

The genes are the units of hereditary information that determine the form and function of the cell and the organism. In diploid cells, genes are present in pairs; one gene of each pair is on one homologous chromosome, while the second is on the other homologous chromosome. There are thousands of gene pairs in any cell, and they are part of the chromosomes. The genes on a chromosome are arranged in a fixed linear order.

Genes act by controlling protein synthesis and consequently enzyme synthesis. Generally, there is one gene for each enzyme. Thus, if ten enzymatic reactions are involved in the formation of a flower pigment, there must be ten genes that govern its production. Genes, while usually highly stable, are capable of change. Such changes are called *mutations* and may result in relatively small or relatively great changes in gene action. The genes constituting a pair may be different. A gene pair, for example, may determine flower color. One gene may give red flowers while another may give white. If the gene for red flowers is dominant, then the flowers will be red when the gene pair consists of at least one red gene. Only plants with two white genes will have white flowers.

Even with this limited amount of information about the genes, several important features of meiosis can be readily understood. First, the importance of the separation and recombination of the homologous chromosomes becomes clear. Through this mechanism, a recombination of genes can be achieved which is impossible to attain through mitosis. Such recombination results in the fullest possible expression of the genetic potential of an interbreeding population. Changes that occur by mutation can be expressed and distributed through the population if they are advantageous. Second, the importance of chiasmata formation is evident. As a result of chiasmata formation, parts of chromatids are exchanged, and different genes are introduced into a chromosome, thus furthering the degree of genetic recombination. Third, the second division of meiosis, through the separation of chromatids, increases still further the number of possible recombinations. The diagram in Fig. 9-3 illustrates all of these points.

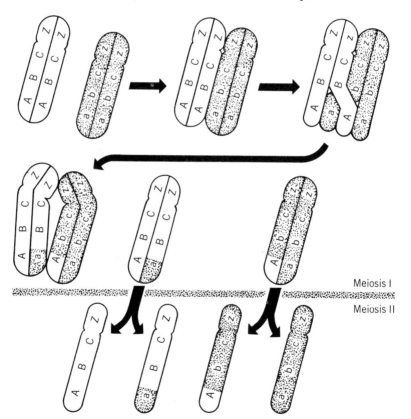

Fig. 9-3. *Importance of meiosis as seen by the distribution of genes. The letters on the chromosomes represent genes.*

Meiosis and gametic fusion produce individuals that are different from one another. These differences are the basis for natural selection and for the adaptation of the organism to the environment. Meiosis is consequently an extremely important process in the continued existence and development of the species.

GENES AND CHROMOSOMES

A gene can be considered a relatively discrete unit located on the chromosome. There is little question that genes are composed of DNA. As noted in Chapter 7, DNA is located primarily in the nucleus as part of the chromatin that forms the chromosomes. The chromosomes are composed of DNA and protein, although it is not yet known how these two chemicals are arranged to form the chromosomes.

The structure of the DNA molecule can be precisely duplicated through the mechanism of base pairing (Fig. 7-5). This is certainly a prerequisite property for a compound that is to function as a bearer of information. The genetic information must be transmitted from one generation to the next with a minimum of variation. That DNA is capable of precise duplication is an important factor in its being considered the genetic material.

Another prerequisite for a molecule that will function as a gene is that it be capable of storing and transmitting information. This poses the question of the nature of the information to be stored and transmitted. The genes are known to act by controlling enzyme synthesis. Enzymes are proteins and as such are composed of amino acids arranged in a specific pattern. If the gene is to influence protein synthesis, the necessary information is the type and order of the amino acids present in the protein. There are, however, some 20 amino acids and only four bases. If the bases of the DNA molecule are the functional units of genetic information, the problem becomes one of coding.

In this case, the code must consist of an arrangement of bases that signifies a particular amino acid. The linear arrangement of the bases forming the code pattern for a number of amino acids would determine the arrangement of the amino acids in the protein. The code must also have a minimum possibility of confusion through the placement of one code set next to another. It would hardly do if two sets placed together formed another code set.

Taking these factors into account, a code system can be devised in which an arrangement of three bases signifies a specific amino acid.

The three bases, of course, need not be different. One message unit of the code may consist of three adenines; another, one adenine and two thymines in a specific arrangement. Although a code in which the message units consist of three parts was first determined on theoretical grounds, it has been demonstrated to exist in the cell through experimental procedures. The code has in fact been unraveled to the point where the bases resulting in the arrangement of specific amino acids can be postulated, as in the following table.

Amino Acid	RNA Code Words			
Alanine	CCG	UCG*		
Arginine	CGC	AGA	UCG*	
Asparagine	ACA	AUA		
Aspartic acid	GUA			
Cysteine	UUG			
Glutamic acid	GAA	AGU*		
Glutamine	ACA	AGA	AGU*	
Glycine	UGG	AGG		
Histidine	ACC			
Isoleucine	UAU	UAA		
Leucine	UUG	UUC	UUA	UUU
Lysine	AAA	AAG*	AAU*	
Methionine	UGA			
Phenylalanine	UUU			
Proline	CCC	CUU*	CCA*	CCG*
Serine	UCU	UCC	UCG	
Threonine	CAC	CAA		
Tryptophan	GGU			
Tyrosine	AUU			
Valine	UGU			

* Uncertain

From this table it is clear that the code is not perfect. In a perfect code there would be only one group of three bases for each amino acid, yet in the postulated code there are many cases in which more than one code unit exists for a particular amino acid. That such duplication is possible in the coding does not imply lack of specificity in the synthesis of the protein. It simply means that more than one way is available by which a specific amino acid can be directed to a

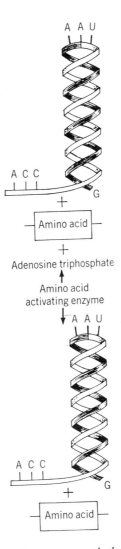

A A U

A C C

G

+

Amino acid

+

Adenosine triphosphate

Amino acid
activating enzyme

A A U

A C C

G

+

Amino acid

Fig. 9-4a. *Diagrammatic summary of the possible sequence of events in the formation of proteins. Transfer RNA is a special helical form of RNA which transports amino acids to their proper site in the protein chain. There is at least one transfer RNA for each of the 20 common amino acids. All, however, seem to carry the bases ACC where the amino acids attach and G at the opposite end. The attachment requires a specific enzyme and energy supplied by adenosine triphosphate. Unpaired bases in transfer RNA (AAU in the example) may provide the means by which transfer RNA "recognizes" the place to deposit its amino-acid package.*

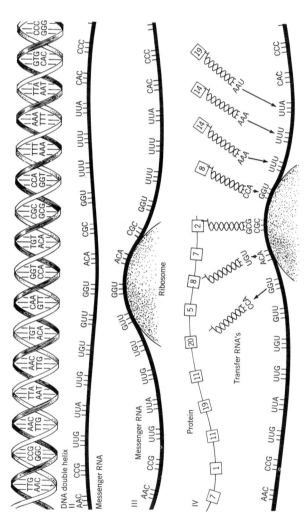

Fig. 9-4b. *Synthesis of protein begins with the genetic code embodied in DNA (1). The code is transcribed into messenger RNA (2). In the diagram, it is assumed that the message has been derived from the DNA strand shown in darker type. The messenger RNA finds its way to a ribosome (3), the site of protein synthesis. Amino acids, indicated by numbered rectangles, are carried to proper sites on the messenger RNA by molecules of transfer RNA (see Fig. 9-5a). Bases are grouped in triplets, and mechanism of recognition between transfer RNA and messenger RNA is hypothetical. Linkage of amino-acid subunits creates a protein molecule. By permission of Scientific American.*

specific site. In the postulated code, the only real difficulty is in the code unit UUU, which codes for the amino acid leucine as well as phenylalanine. But this is a minor problem in light of the total code and the versatility and specificity that it contains.

Thus, a gene can be considered a piece of DNA large enough to contain the code necessary for the formation of an enzyme molecule. A mutation in these terms is a change in the code through a change in the composition of the DNA molecule.

An average protein molecule contains roughly 200 amino acids. All or most of the 20 amino acids are probably present and arranged in a specific pattern. The gene must therefore contain 200 precisely arranged code units, each composed of three bases. Thus, a total of 600 bases are involved on the average in the production of a single protein. Clearly, it is important not only that the code units be correct and meaningful and that they be arranged properly, but that they be read correctly. How this is accomplished is still not understood, but evidence suggests that mechanisms are present to prohibit or reduce the chance of misreading the message coded in the DNA.

GENES, DNA, AND RNA

This concept of the gene closes the gap between the hereditary information and the mechanism of protein synthesis. The sequence can be outlined as follows (see Fig. 9-4). A segment of DNA contains the information for the assembly of a group of amino acids into a specific protein. This information exists in the form of the arrangement of triplets of pyridine and purine bases composing the DNA molecule. Through RNA synthesis in the nucleus mediated by this DNA, the information is transferred to the RNA molecule. The information in the RNA molecule is again represented in the form of a three-part code based on the four bases, and this RNA (the messenger RNA of Chapter 6) moves to the cytoplasm. Here, the messenger RNA acts as the template for the synthesis of protein molecules; this synthesis takes place at the ribosomes and involves an additional RNA (transfer RNA, Chapter 6), which is amino acid specific and which is also coded. The end product is an enzyme molecule that mediates a specific chemical reaction in the cell.

This outline of the gene-enzyme relationship presents only a simple summary and does not reflect the tremendous diversity of interactions and complications that exist. Neither does it reflect interrelationships in the metabolism of the cell not directly related to the gene.

10

THE PROBLEM

OF CELL

DEVELOPMENT

The typical cell is one of the grand illusions of biology. Like the average man, it is much discussed but infrequently met.

The actual cells that compose the individuals of the plant kingdom range from one extreme to another in their morphology, physiology, and biochemistry. If only the vascular plants are considered for the moment, the number of different types of cells present is huge and each type varies from the other cells of the plant not only in its mature stage but in the various stages of its development. These differences are present at all levels of the morphological and physiological organization of the cell. Some of these differences can be seen in the cells of the root tip.

The root tips of vascular plants have been widely studied in their cell development by morphological, physiological, and biochemical means. The reason for this concentration on the root tip is that it is a rapidly developing system that can be easily studied. Roots are easily obtained by germinating seeds or starting bulbs, their gross morphology is extremely regular, and they can be readily treated with a variety of experimental agents. Finally, they are not difficult to prepare for examination with the light and electron microscopes.

The root tip consists first of a cap that covers the extreme end of the root and extends back for a variable distance from the end of the root. The cap surrounds a group of cells known as the *apical initials*. These cells are the starting point of the files of the cells composing the root and, while not actively dividing under normal conditions, they are important in the organization of the root. Above the apical initials, the major tissues of the root can be distinguished. Starting from the outside of the root, these are the *epidermis,* the *cortex,* and the *vascular cylinder,* which can be divided into the *xylem,* or water carrying cells, and the *phloem,* which transports organic matter. Each of these groups of cells can be divided further into more specialized cell types, which will not be discussed here.

The cells of the root, like the other cells of the plant, have a definite life span and show a wide range of states of development. Thus, development may be rapid in young cells, or it may be slow as the cells reach their final maturation stages. Thus, in the root tip the cells immediately behind the apical initials are relatively small and rapidly dividing. Farther from the tip, although still dividing, they begin to increase in length. Next, divisions become infrequent and the cells increase in length at a much faster rate. Many other changes occur

		Apical cells	Radial enlargement	Beginning elongation	Rapid elongation
DNA					
	Amount	2C	2C ► 4C	2C ► 4C ► 8C	4C ► 8C
	Synthesis	None	Correlated with mitosis	Continues although mitosis ceasing	Not correlated with mitosis
RNA - Protein	synthesis breakdown	None	Synthesis-no breakdown	Synthesis and breakdown equal	Synthesis and breakdown equal
Cell wall					
	Pectins	Low	Increasing	Medium	Same
	Hemi-cellulose	Low	Increasing	Medium	Same
	Noncellulosic polysaccharides	Low	Low	Increasing	High
	Cellulose	Low	Low	Increasing	High

Fig. 10-1. *Chart of changes in various activities and constituents of the plant cell during development. Data taken from analyses of root tips.*

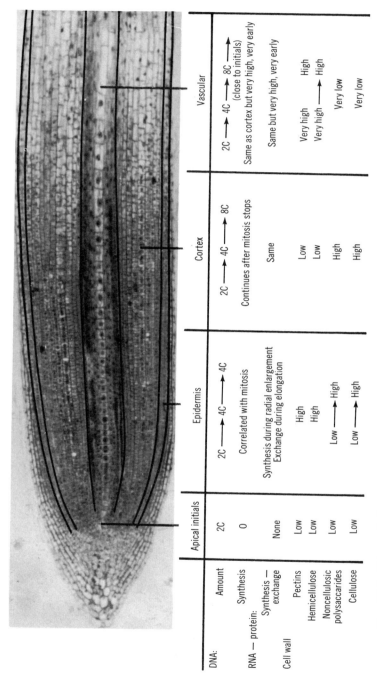

	Apical initials	Epidermis	Cortex	Vascular
DNA: Amount	2C	2C → 4C → 4C	2C → 4C → 8C	2C → 4C → 8C (close to initials)
RNA — protein: Synthesis	0	Correlated with mitosis	Continues after mitosis stops	Same as cortex but very high, very early
Synthesis — exchange	None	Synthesis during radial enlargement / Exchange during elongation	Same	Same but very high, very early
Cell wall: Pectins	Low	High	Low	Very high → High
Hemicellulose	Low	High	Low	Very high → High
Noncellulosic polysaccharides	Low	Low → High	High	Very low
Cellulose	Low	Low → High	High	Very low

Fig. 10-2. Chart of changes in various activities and constituents during development of the cells of various tissues found in the root tip.

during this phase of growth, which ends as cell elongation ceases. The end of elongation does not mean that all development ceases in a cell; in fact, a wide range of subsequent changes take place as the cell matures. Moreover, while all of the cells of the root are undergoing these generalized changes, each tissue and cell type is developing in its unique pattern.

These two points can be seen in Figs. 10-1 and 10-2. The data presented in Fig. 10-1 are of the changes in composition and activity of the average cell in the stages of development that occur in the first two millimeters of the onion root tip. These data are sufficient to characterize certain aspects of the various stages of cell development. They indicate that respiration, as measured by oxygen consumption, is low in rapidly dividing cells and high in rapidly elongating cells. They also show that DNA synthesis is first correlated with mitosis but then, as mitosis ceases, DNA synthesis continues and the amount of DNA increases per nucleus. Cell-wall composition also changes as the cells develop. The young cells contain relatively large amounts of pectic substances and hemicellulose, whereas the older cells contain relatively larger amounts of noncellulosic polysaccharides and cellulose.

While these patterns of development are meaningful when the root is considered as being composed of generalized cells, they are not accurate for any given tissue or cell type. Consequently, when the data is expressed in terms of the various tissues, almost endless variations on the general theme become apparent. From Fig. 10-2 it is evident that although the cells of the cortex follow the generalized pattern for DNA synthesis, the epidermal cells cease DNA synthesis when mitosis ceases. On the other hand, the amount of DNA in the vascular cells increases out of phase with mitosis at a very early stage of development. Similar changes are also apparent in wall composition. Each tissue shows a distinct pattern of wall development in terms of wall constituents.

Differences in cells are also apparent when they are examined with the electron microscope. The cells shown in Fig. 10-3 are of the onion root tip. Those forming the outer layers are cells of the cap, the slightly elongated ones are epidermal cells, and the innermost are cortical cells. Differences of vacuoles, ER, mitochondria, plastids, Golgi bodies, and nuclei among the various cells are readily apparent.

There have been intensive studies of changes in the ultrastructure of the cells of corn root by a group of investigators at the University

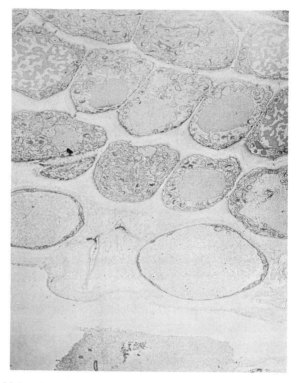

Fig. 10-3. *Electron-microscope photograph of the root cap and epidermal cells of onion root tip.*

of Texas directed by W. G. Whaley. These studies have established the role of the Golgi body in cell-wall formation and have revealed a host of changes in the subcellular components associated with the development of the cells. Careful electron-microscope observations of the ultrastructural changes that accompany the development of phloem cells have been made by Katherine Esau of the University of California. These amazing cells lose their nuclei as they become functional in sugar transport. The distinction between vacuole and cytoplasm is also lost.

The number of examples of differences in vascular-plant cells at all levels of organization is in itself immense. The point is that while generalizations can be made concerning cell structure and function, the most valid generalization of all is that cells differ from one another in a great many ways. The question that immediately arises from such a statement is, How do these differences become established?

THE PROBLEM OF CELL DIFFERENTIATION

The problem of how cells become different is perhaps the most basic of the unanswered questions of biology. Certain aspects of the problem are common to both animal and plant cells. There are a number of unique features of plant cells, however, that are important in cell differentiation. One is the wall.

The presence of a rigid wall means that the cells are stationary. Thus, cell-migration and cell-position effects, so important in animal cell development, are minimal. What assumes great importance is the phenomenon of unequal cell division. There are many examples of the importance of unequal divisions in plants. These include (1) the first division of the zygote nucleus, (2) the pollen nucleus, (3) the cell that will form the phloem cell and the companion cell, (4) the cell that gives rise to the first xylem cell, and (5) the cell that will form the root-hair cell. The last example has been intensively studied by modern methods, which have revealed some of the features of this type of development.

Root hairs normally occur several millimeters back from the tip. They consist of long protrusions of epidermal cells into the soil, and are important in the absorption of water and minerals from the soil. Not all epidermal cells have hairs. In certain grasses, the cells that have hairs alternate in a regular fashion with cells that do not, providing an interesting experimental system. The epidermal cells nearest the tip undergo a series of divisions. The daughter cells of these early divisions are equal in size and do not give rise to hairs. The last division, however, is unequal, one cell being markedly smaller than the other. It is the smaller cell that forms the hair. In the vast majority of cases, the smaller cell is the energetic cell—that is, the cell that goes on in development or forms the more elaborate structure.

Work by Charlotte Avers at Rutgers University has shown clearly that the enzyme content of the cell that forms the hair is different and higher than the cell that does not. Differences in growth rate also have been measured. There is considerable evidence that the cells that are the products of an unequal division are different shortly after their formation. It seems, in fact, that the unequal division is the result of a decided polarity in the mother cell and that the unequal division is the result of an unequal distribution of the cytoplasm of the mother cell. The division results in the compartmentalization of the elements of the mother cell resulting in the formation of energetic and non-energetic daughter cells. This division of labor has great effects on the development of the cell.

The immediate question is why an unequal division should cause such profound effects. The answer is by no means clear; indeed, it would be accurate to say that not even the outline of an answer is clear. Yet several points can be made that at least illustrate the basic problem of cell differentiation.

As discussed in Chapter 8, mitosis provides for the exact duplication of the chromosomes and the nucleus in two daughter cells. The genes, which are assumed to direct protein synthesis, are precisely replicated. Consequently, the genetic constitution of the daughter nuclei is identical. Each nucleus in the same individual has the same, or very close to the same, initial gene content. That the various nuclei are similar and contain all the genes necessary for development can be shown by the fact that most cells of the plant can, under proper conditions, give rise to an entire plant. Thus, a single cell in the plant has the capacity to differentiate into all types of cells, yet it normally develops into only a single type. The answer to this problem of individual cell development must come not from the gene content of the nucleus but from the ways in which the genes are expressed. The levels at which the regulation of gene expression can possibly occur are many.

There is evidence, for example, of interactions between the nucleus and the cytoplasm, so that changes in the cytoplasm are reflected in the nucleus. An example of such a change may occur in the unequal division preceding root hair development. In this case, the nuclear division results in essentially identical nuclei but these nuclei are associated with quite different types of cytoplasm. Thus, if the direction of differentiation is determined by an interaction between the nucleus and cytoplasm, quite different types of interaction may result in the two cells, giving rise to different patterns of development. If this is true, the problem becomes one of understanding both this interaction and the factors that initially lead to the unequal division.

Interaction between the cytoplasm and the nucleus may take the form of activating or inactivating genes. Under a given set of conditions, one group of genes may be active while another group may be inactive because of the presence, for example, of various proteins. Any change in these conditions, such as an unequal cell division, the addition of a specific growth substance, or a change in the environment in the immediate region of the cell, may be enough to change the pattern of gene action and modify the direction of differentiation.

This type of gene activation has been proposed to explain the conversion of the stem apex from vegetative growth to flower formation after the arrival of the flowering hormone from the leaves. At the present time, these suggestions must be regarded as speculations and not as explanations.

On a different level, less directly related to gene action, is the interaction of various enzymes and enzyme systems. Thus, the relative rates of reaction of two competing enzyme systems under a given set of conditions may determine which system will utilize the available substrate. The difference in possible end products may result in different pathways of development. The effect of growth regulators on enzyme systems may, in a similar manner, govern the course of cell differentiation. Various types of feedback mechanisms may also be involved. An example of a feedback mechanism is when the product of the reaction, in sufficient quantity, will inhibit the reaction producing it until the end product is removed. In the case of a multienzyme system, an increased concentration of the final end product will frequently inhibit all the reactions in the series. If there are alternate pathways for the utilization of the available substrate, the action of a feedback mechanism may be the determining factor in the course of the differentiation of a cell. How important any of these mechanisms are in the actual course of cell differentiation remains to be shown by careful experimentation.

In any consideration of the factors important in the ultimate direction of cell development and differentiation, it is important to remember that a number of mechanisms are in all probability operating at the same time. Thus, D. Foard and A. Haber of Oak Ridge National Laboratory have been able to demonstrate that in seedlings resulting from the germination of seeds treated with massive doses of gamma radiation, normal-appearing leaves will be produced without cell division. In the seeds they used, the leaf primordia were present and at germination the cells expanded to a much greater extent than they would have normally. Thus, because there were no cell divisions, the leaf was composed of many fewer cells but each cell was larger. The important point in their work is that the leaves reached their normal size and shape. Therefore, cell divisions could not have determined the size or the shape of the leaves. These were determined by other factors present in the cells at the time of irradiation and were expressed during subsequent development. Another fact is important in this work: specialized cells such as guard cells did not develop. Since these cells are the result of divisions that occur only after the leaf has emerged from the seed, they are never formed. Thus, while cell divisions are not a determining factor in leaf size or shape, they are important in cell differentiation. This work makes the further important point that an organ of a plant is more than the simple sum of the cells present. Factors based on the interaction between cells appear of considerable importance in determining the course of both cell and tissue development.

Knowledge of the factors directing cell development is being expanded constantly. One of the major reasons for the current interest in the problem is that the advances being made by the molecular biologists can now be applied to this area. The mechanisms of gene action and the nature of the genetic material provide a starting point for future work on the problem of differentiation. But a starting point is all they provide. The elucidation of the mechanism of cell differentiation will come only through the continued study of cell morphology, physiology, and biochemistry at all levels of organization and at every stage of development. Although the world of the cell is becoming a much more familiar place, there are still vast unexplored regions and still more worlds to conquer.

SUGGESTIONS FOR

FURTHER READING

Allfrey, V. G., and A. E. Mirsky. "How Cells Make Molecules." *Scientific American,* Vol. 205 (Sept. 1961), pp. 74–82.

Andrade, E. N. da C. "Robert Hooke." In *Lives in Science,* ed. *Scientific American.* New York: Simon and Schuster, Inc., 1957.

Arnon, D. I. "The Role of Light in Photosynthesis." *Scientific American,* Vol. 203 (Nov. 1960), pp. 104–109.

Bassham, J. A. "The Path of Carbon in Photosynthesis." *Scientific American,* Vol. 206 (June 1962), pp. 88–100.

Bogorad, L. "Photosynthesis." In *Plant Biology Today,* ed. W. A. Jensen and L. G. Kavaljian. Belmont, Calif.: Wadsworth Publishing Company, Inc., 1963.

Bonner, J. "Molecular Botany." In *Plant Biology Today,* ed. W. A. Jensen and L. G. Kavaljian. Belmont, Calif.: Wadsworth Publishing Company, Inc., 1963.

Brachet, J. "The Living Cell." *Scientific American,* Vol. 205 (Sept. 1961), pp. 50–61.

Crick, F. H. C. "The Genetic Code." *Scientific American,* Vol. 207 (Oct. 1962), pp. 67–72.

Green, D. "The Synthesis of Fat." *Scientific American,* Vol. 202 (Feb. 1960), pp. 46–51.

Holter, H. "How Things Get into Cells." *Scientific American,* Vol. 205 (Sept. 1961), pp. 167–174.

Hurwitz, J., and J. J. Furth. "Messenger RNA." *Scientific American,* Vol. 206 (Feb. 1962), pp. 41–49.

Jensen, W. A. "The Problem of Cell Development in Plants." In *Plant Biology Today,* ed. W. A. Jensen and L. G. Kavaljian. Belmont, Calif.: Wadsworth Publishing Company, Inc., 1963.

Kendrew, J. C. "Three-Dimensional Study of a Protein Molecule." *Scientific American,* Vol. 205 (Dec. 1961), pp. 96–110.

Lehninger, A. L. "Energy Transformation in the Cell." *Scientific American,* Vol. 202 (May 1960), pp. 102–111.

——————. "How Cells Transform Energy." *Scientific American,* Vol. 205 (Sept. 1961), pp. 62–73.

Mazia, D. "How Cells Divide." *Scientific American,* Vol. 205 (Sept. 1961), pp. 100–108.

Nirenberg, M. W. "The Genetic Code II." *Scientific American,* Vol. 208 (Mar. 1963), pp. 80–86.

Nord, F. F., and W. J. Schubert. "Lignin." *Scientific American,* Vol. 199 (Oct. 1958), pp. 104–110.

Preston, R. D. "Cellulose." *Scientific American,* Vol. 197 (Sept. 1957), pp. 156–160.

Rich, A. "Polyribosomes." *Scientific American,* Vol. 209 (Dec. 1963), pp. 44–53.

Robertson, J. D. "Membrane of the Living Cell." *Scientific American,* Vol. 206 (Apr. 1962), pp. 64–72.

Schmitt, F. O. "Giant Molecules in Cells and Tissues." *Scientific American,* Vol. 197 (Sept. 1957), pp. 204–206.

Stein, W. H., and S. Moore. "The Chemical Structure of Proteins." *Scientific American,* Vol. 204 (Feb. 1961), pp. 81–86.

Wald, G. "Life and Light." *Scientific American,* Vol. 201 (Oct. 1959), pp. 92–100.

GLOSSARY

Activation energy. The energy at which molecules are no longer stable. Enzymes act by reducing the activation energy of a reaction.

Adenosine triphosphate (ATP). A compound containing high-energy phosphate groups. The removal of one results in the formation of adenosine diphosphate (ADP) and the release of energy to the cell. The process is reversible, so that ADP plus phosphate plus enough energy will yield ATP.

Aerobic respiration. The biological process in which, in the presence of oxygen, carbohydrates are converted through a series of complex reactions to carbon dioxide and water with the release of energy.

Amino acids. Compounds containing an amino group which form the basic units in protein structure. There are approximately 20 amino acids.

Amyloplasts. Plastids specialized for the storage of starch.

Anaphase. The stage of nuclear division during which the centromeres divide and the chromatids of each chromosome separate and move to the opposite poles.

Angstrom (A). A unit of measure: 1 A = 1/10,000 mm.

Apposition. Growth by the addition of layers of material to the wall.

Carotenoids. Yellow to red pigments found in chloroplasts and chromoplasts.

Cell plate. The first-formed wall structure in a dividing cell.

Cell wall. The rigid outermost covering of the plant cell.

Cellulose. A chemical component of the cell wall consisting of large molecules composed of glucose units.

Centrioles. Small bodies, usually in pairs, situated in the cytoplasm near the nucleus, and involved in the formation of the spindle.

Centromere. The point of attachment of the spindle fiber to the chromosome.

Chiasmata. The points at which the homologous chromosomes remain attached during the later stages of prophase of meiosis I.

Chitin. A chemical component of the walls of many fungi consisting of a complex molecule composed of carbohydrate derivatives that contain nitrogen groups.

Chlorophyll. A green pigment localized in the chloroplasts that absorb the light energy used in photosynthesis.

Chloroplasts. Plastids containing chlorophyll and other pigment. Chloroplasts are the site of photosynthesis in the cell.

Chromatid. One-half of a chromosome. Two chromatids joined in the region of the centromere constitute a chromosome.

Chromatin. The nuclear material that makes up the genetic material of the cell.

Chromoplast. A type of plastid that contains concentrations of pigments other than chlorophyll.

Chromosomes. Morphologically distinct units in the nucleus, composed of chromatin. Chromosomes are the sites of the genes.

Clear zone. The area around the prophase nucleus free of the larger cell parts. The clear zone is believed involved in the formation of the spindle.

Cristae. The internal projections of the inner mitochondrial membrane.

Cyclosis. The streaming of the cytoplasm in the living cell. It is most frequently observed in vacuolate cells.

Cytochromes. Compounds involved in electron transfer. They contain iron, ring groups, and a protein.

Cytokinesis. The process in which a cell is divided into two or more cells, usually by the formation of walls.

Cytoplasm. The living matter of the cell exclusive of the nucleus.

Deoxyribonucleic acid (DNA). A chemical component of the cell composed of repeating units containing nitrogen bases and believed to be the genetic material of the cell.

Deoxyribose. A specific five-carbon sugar found only in DNA.

Dictyosomes. Cytoplasmic particles consisting of several layers of lamellae surrounded by small vesicles. The term may be used as a synonym for Golgi bodies or as a specific type of Golgi body.

Differential permeability. The property of a membrane to pass selectively certain molecules more freely than others.

Diploid. A nucleus with chromosomes present in sets of pairs.

Direct oxidation pathway. The breakdown of glucose to CO_2 and water, not involving the Krebs cycle, with the net gain of 36 ATP molecules.

Electron transport. The sequence of chemical events involved in the transfer of electrons from one energy level to another. During this transfer, energy is made available to the cell.

Electron-transport particles. The morphological site of the enzymes involved in electron transport.

Elongation. Growth of a cell by increase in length.

Endoplasmic reticulum (ER). A system of membranes that permeate the cytoplasm of the cell. The ER may or may not have ribosomes associated with it.

Energy of activation. The energy required to render molecules capable of reaction.

Enzyme. An organic catalyst involved in many reactions that take place in the cell. Composed of protein, enzymes reduce the activation energy of the reactions in which they are involved.

Equatorial plane. The plane midway between the two daughter nuclei of a dividing cell.

Fatty acids. The basic unit in the formation of fats and lipids.

Fermentation. The breakdown of glucose, in the absence of oxygen, to ethyl alcohol and CO_2 with the release of energy.

Flavoprotein. Compounds involved in the electron-transport system and closely associated with the cytochromes.

Free energy. A property of a substance which may define its ability to diffuse; diffusion occurs along a gradient from high to low free energy.

Gene. The basic heredity unit of the cell.

Glucose. A six-carbon sugar, $C_6H_{12}O_6$.

Glycolysis. The breakdown of glucose into two pyruvic acid molecules.

Golgi bodies. A type of cytoplasmic particle found in cells throughout the plant and animal kingdoms. (See *Dictyosomes.*)

Grana. Specialized thickening in the lamellar system of the chloroplast.

Haploid. The base number of chromosomes present in a nucleus, each chromosome being represented singly.

Hemicellulose. A chemical component of the cell wall rich in five-carbon sugars.

Hexose. The general class of sugars containing six-carbon atoms.

Hexuronic acids. Acids derived from six-carbon sugars (hexoses) found predominantly in the pectic substances and the hemicellulose of the cell wall.

Histones. Proteins, rich in basic amino acids, found in the nucleus and associated with the chromosomes and nucleolus.

Homologous chromosomes. Chromosomes so similar that they can pair during meiosis. Also, the pairs of chromosomes present in a diploid nucleus.

Intercalary growth. Growth of the cell wall by the insertion of new microfibrils of material into the wall.

Karyokinesis. The division of the nucleus.

Krebs cycle. The ultimate breakdown of the two-carbon compound produced by the modification of pyruvic acid to CO_2 and water with the release of energy.

Lamellae. Membranes that occur in plastids and form the basic structural unit of the chloroplasts.

Leucoplasts. Plastids containing no visible pigments or stored food.

Lignin. A chemical component of the cell wall which lends it considerable strength and rigidity; the major noncarbohydrate component of the wall.

Lipid. A chemical component of the cell which consists of three fatty acids and glycol.

Lysosomes. Small cytoplasmic bodies surrounded by a single unit membrane and containing enzymes believed to aid in the digestion of intercellular or extracellular material. Their existence in plant cells is uncertain at present.

Meiosis. A nuclear division in which the chromosome number is halved. Meiosis consists of two divisions, during which the homologous chromosomes first pair, then separate, and finally replicate.

Messenger RNA. The RNA that is produced in the nucleus and that moves to the cytoplasm. It determines the sequence of amino acids in the protein molecule.

Metaphase. The stage of nuclear division during which the chromosomes are situated on the equatorial plate.

Microfibril. The very fine fibers, composed primarily of cellulose, which form part of the cell wall.

Micron (μ). A unit of measure. 1 micron $= 1/1000$ millimeters.

Middle lamella. That region of the wall common to two cells; the outermost layer of the cell wall. The middle lamella is composed primarily of pectic substances.

Mitochondria. Small cytoplasmic organelles, usually rod or spherical in shape, involved in aerobic respiration.

Mitosis. The division of the nucleus which results in each of the two new nuclei having the same number of chromosomes.

Molecule. The basic unit of chemical organization of the cell. Molecules are composed of groups of atoms.

Mutations. A permanent change in a gene such that the heredity of the organism is altered.

Nitrogen bases. Adenine, guanine, cytosine, thymine, and uracil. The nitrogen bases are found in the nucleic acids.

Nuclear membrane. The double membrane surrounding the nucleus.

Nuclear pores. Openings in the nuclear membrane. They may be true openings or they may be filled with a plug.

Nuclear sap. That portion of the nucleus other than the chromatin and nucleolus; it is liquid or semi-liquid in consistency.

Nucleolus. A small dense body, rich in RNA and protein, found in the nucleus. Frequently more than one nucleolus is present.

Nucleus. A large structure, found in nearly all cells, which is the site of the genetic material of the cell.

Osmosis. Diffusion of solvent (water) molecules in response to a free-energy gradient of these molecules through a differentially permeable membrane that allows more rapid passage of solvent than solute molecules.

Pectic substances. Compounds composed primarily of hexuronic acids found in the cell wall.

Pentoses. Sugars containing five-carbon atoms.

Phosphoglyceric acid (PGA). The substance believed to be the first stable compound produced during the CO_2 fixation stage of photosynthesis.

Photosynthesis. The biochemical process in which electromagnetic energy is transformed into chemical energy.

Phragmoplast. The modified spindle region at the equatorial plate after the chromosomes have moved to the poles; it is involved in the formation of the cell plate.

Pinocytosis. A process in which substances enter cells by first being absorbed on the plasma membrane and then being transferred inside the cell by the invagination of the membrane.

Pits. Holes in the cell wall.

Plasma membrane. The unit membrane surrounding the outer layer of the cytoplasm.

Plasmodesmata. Cytoplasmic connections between cells which extend through the wall.

Plastids. A class of cytoplasmic organelle involved principally in the formation and storage of carbohydrates.

Polysaccharide. A carbohydrate composed of many simple sugars united in a large molecule.

Polysomes. Groups of ribosomes associated with a strand of messenger RNA involved in the production of protein.

Primary wall. The usually thin wall found surrounding the growing cell.

Prophase. The stage of nuclear division during which the chromosomes become visible.

Proplastid. An immature or newly formed plastid.

Protein. A large molecule composed of many amino acids. Proteins form one of the most important classes of compounds found in the cell.

Pyrenoid. A specialized structure within a chloroplast involved in starch synthesis and storage. Pyrenoids are found primarily in the algae.

Pyridine nucleotide. One of a group of compounds involved in energy-transformation reactions during electron transport.

Quantasome. The fundamental unit of organization of the chloroplast.

Respiration. The biologically controlled breakdown of energy-containing substances with the release of energy.

Ribonucleic acid (RNA). One of the two nucleic acids found in plant and animal cells; composed of repeating units of ribose, phosphate, and the nitrogen bases guanine, cytosine, uracil, and adenine.

Ribosomes. Small hemispherical cytoplasmic particles (250 A in diameter) composed of ribonucleic acid and protein; believed essential for protein synthesis.

Saccharides. Sugars; carbohydrates consisting of carbon, oxygen, and hydrogen atoms.

Secondary wall. The cell wall, usually rich in lignin, formed after elongation has ceased.

Spherosomes. Cytoplasmic particles, seen to move rapidly through the cytoplasm, which may be involved in fat synthesis and storage.

Spindle. A collection of fibers that extend from the centromeres to the opposite ends of the region of the cell occupied by the nucleus.

Stroma. The nonlamellar phase of the chloroplast in which photosynthetic phosphorylation is believed to occur.

Telophase. The final stage of nuclear division, during which the chromosomes become diffuse and the nuclear membrane is re-established.

Tip growth. The growth of a cell only at the ends or at a localized area such as in the case of root hairs.

Transfer RNA. The amino acid specific RNA involved in the early stages of protein synthesis.

Unit membrane. The basic unit of the membrane system of the cell; it consists of two layers of protein with a center of lipid molecules.

Vacuole. The usually large, centrally located portion of the plant cell limited by a unit membrane and filled with dilute salt and sugar solution.

INDEX